KU-218-850

Nelson Art Guide

A CREATIVE TOUR THROUGH OUR INSPIRING REGION

The Nelson Art Guide places a stethoscope against the heart of Nelson's creative pulse and features a comprehensive directory of our region's artists.

Whether you're reading this from within or afar, we invite you to view our art, meet our people and experience our place.

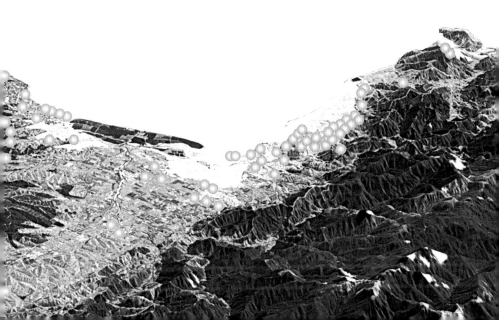

Nelson Bays Arts Advocacy & Marketing Trust retains copyright to the material prepared by the trust and commissioned for this publication and to the overall presentation of the supplied material. Individual advertisers retain copyright to their own information and illustrations.

Disclaimer: All reasonable efforts have been made to ensure the accuracy of the contents at the time of printing. The publisher accepts no responsibility or liability for errors, inaccuracies, omissions or changes in respect of the information.

The information provided in the listings has been provided by the artists and businesses concerned and is not necessarily the opinion of the Nelson Art Guide or Nelson Bays Arts Advocacy & Marketing Trust.

Printed with vegetable inks on recyclable paper created from well managed forests that comply with environmentally sustainable practice and principles.

Published by Nelson Bays Arts Advocacy & Marketing Trust

PO Box 860, Nelson, New Zealand

P: 03 539 0828

E: enquiries@nelsonart.info

W: www.nelsonart.info

First edition 1994, ISBN 0-473-02838-7
Second edition 1997, ISBN 0-473-04437-4
Third edition 2000, ISBN 0-473-06999-7
Fourth edition 2002, ISBN 0-473-08788-X
Fifth edition 2004, ISBN 0-476-00803-4
Sixth edition 2006, ISBN 10:0-473-11367-8 and
ISBN 13:978-0-473-11367-4
Seventh edition 2008, ISBN 978-0-473-13753-3

Awaroa Bay, Abel Tasman National Park. Photo: Ian Trafford

Nelson, the second oldest city in the youngest country on earth has long been a magnet to the metal of creative souls. People have come here on holiday and never wanted to leave. So they didn't.

Over the decades those born with the region's earth in their blood have welcomed, worked alongside, and learned from the like-minded immigrants from distant shores. They've swapped, shared and merged skills, materials and ideas, connecting through their mutual love for art and this place. Together they have woven a unique creative fabric that sustains and inspires the entire community and its guests.

Artists are human magpies, wooed by the glean of Nelson's sun-drenched skies and shimmering azure bays. They long to give eternal life to the greens of the trees and the rolling plains, and solve the rubix cube of colour in the markets, orchards, gardens and groves.

As well as being easy on the eye, Nelson's landscapes house raw materials: Moutere clays that can be moulded into functional forms, Takaka marble that can be carved into sculpture, and timber that can be turned into furniture. In Golden Bay, you can find kokowai (red earth) and grind the sacred stone of the area's tangata whenua (Maori) to literally paint the earth.

But Nelson is, above all, about people. The artists here are approachable and intriguing, acclaimed yet humble, and welcome visitors into their homes, studios, galleries and lives.

Enjoy meeting them.

Paint brushes. Photo: Daniel Allen

Contents

Introducing Your Host

Theres nothing quite like a local's advice. Matt Lawrey acts as your personal tour guide throughout this book introducing you to each areas people and places.

While many New Zealanders know him as the face of Lotto on television, Matt is also an award-winning broadcaster, journalist with a nose for a good local yarn, arts enthusiast who has coordinated four Nelson sculpture symposiums, and is an imported Nelsonian with unmatchable passion for this place.

Matt writes for The Leader community newspaper, is a columnist for The Nelson Mail, reviews films for newspapers around the country, and co-hosted two series of the programme Business Is Booming.

He also hosts a show on Nelson's creative-friendly community radio station Fresh FM — check it out by tuning in on 104.8FM.

Matt Lawrey (above). Max Sculpture Symposium in Trafalger Street (below). Photo: Nelson Mail

Wakefield Quay House (above) and ceramic bowl by Christine Boswijk (below). Photos: Daniel Allen

It was a small turquoise ceramic Christine Boswijk bowl with a twisted spoon that did it.

When I moved to Nelson in 1997 I was lucky enough to spend a year in a house on the waterfront packed with local art. The place was stuffed with artwork by the likes of Sally Burton, Jens Hansen, Darryl Frost, Katie Gold and Owen Bartlett.

Growing up I had developed some pretty unimaginative ideas about art. Art was serious stuff. It was not frivolous, it was not cheerful and most of all it was not colourful. My myopic and monochromatic sensibilities made living with all that Nelson art a challenge. For the life of me, I could not imagine why anyone would want to be surrounded by that much colour.

But the longer I lived there, the less confronting those artworks became. The more time I spent in the sun, the more I swam in Tasman Bay, the more I visited places like Marahau and the more I experienced events like the Nelson Arts Festival's Masked Parade, the more I connected with both the colour and the art around me. Nelson has that effect on people.

Before long, I even found myself liking the house's paintings, sculptures and pottery, although that small turquoise bowl was the last to win my affections.

The more I looked at it, the more I wondered who had made it and what else they might be capable of. Finally, I asked a flatmate for the artist's name and soon, with a map scribbled on a wine-stained serviette, I was in the car heading for Christine's studio near Mapua.

I don't think I'm exaggerating when I tell you that visit was a significant event in my life. I loved the drive, I loved Christine's studio, I loved her work, I loved Christine and I loved buying my own small turquoise bowl with a twisted spoon.

Sir Toss Wollaston (above). Photo: David Wayne. View from Takaka Hill painting by Toss Woollaston (below). Photo: The Suter Art Gallery

Dedication

This edition of the Nelson Art Guide is dedicated to Sir Mountford Tosswill (Toss) Woollaston, 1910-1998.

One of New Zealand's foremost landscape painters, Toss was a pioneer of the modern art movement in New Zealand and was knighted for services to art in 1979. New Zealand poet Charles Brasch described him as "one of the first to see and paint New Zealand as a New Zealander". His work is said to have changed the way New Zealanders viewed their landscape.

Toss spent the greater part of his years in the Nelson region. His first studio home was built by hand from bricks of local clay on an orchard in Mapua in 1934.

A man of renowned spirit, his vibrant life palette of talent, struggles and successes has imprinted a legacy in this place that has and will long inspire Nelson's artists.

Using the Nelson Art Guide

The directory listings in this book are mapped out as trails throughout the region from Cable Bay to Golden Bay.

As well as artists, galleries, wineries, cafés and other creatively based experiences, you'll find information about significant sites and public artworks in the surrounding areas.

Follow the full creative trail from bay to bay, seek artists in a specific area, or flick through and select a few favourites. If you are interested in a particular art form, there is also a quick reference that lists artists by discipline in the index at the back of the book.

How to use the maps

Each artist listing has a number that relates to both their number on the map and their page number in the book so you can easily locate the artist on the trail. The coresponding map reference is at the top of each artists page.

Sightseeing

Go sightseeing Nelson-style and see how artists have interpreted various sites and landscapes throughout the region. Throughout the guide artworks from The Suter Art Gallery's historic collection are accompanied by images from photographer Marion Van Dijk, which capture the scenes as they are today.

Visitors at Katie Gold & Owen Bartlett's ceramic studio. Photo: Nelson Tasman Tourism

Visiting Artists

While a number of the artists listed in this book are open regular hours, others invite viewing by appointment.

For many artists, being available to meet by appointment rather than set hours simply gives them the freedom creative spirits need.

The accessibility and welcoming nature of our artists is something that Nelson prides itself on. Even if you're just keen to look, by all means pick up the phone. Making an appointment to view work does not mean signing up to buy; there's no expectation, just an open door.

Sending Artwork Home

Art is not always the most travel-friendly purchase. We want you to have a smashing time here, but preferably not literally. Many outlets across the region offer a professional packaging and consignment service. Purchases posted overseas may even be tax free, which will save you 12.5 % in goods and services tax.

When purchasing work, ask for advice on how to best transport and care for your new acquisition. Alternatively, visit New Zealand Post's outlets throughout the region. (refer www.nzpost.co.nz)

Kathryn Furniss outside her studio (above). Sealevel Studio in Tasman (below). Photos: Daniel Allen

Getting Around

By far the easiest way to see the Nelson region is to hop in a car and hit the road.

The maps in this book will help you find where you want to go. Use the below as a guide to how long it will take you to get around the region.

Location to destination	Km's	Time
Nelson City to Cable Bay	14	20 mins
Nelson City to Richmond	14	20 mins
Nelson City to Brightwater	22	30 mins
Nelson City to St Arnaud	109	1 hr 20 mins
Nelson City to Mapua	33	30 mins
Nelson City to Motueka	50	45 mins
Motueka to Kaiteriteri	14	20 mins
Motueka to Marahau	18	25 mins
Motueka to Takaka	58	60 mins
Takaka to Collingwood	27	35 mins

While the Nelson Art Guide tries to make it as easy as possible to find what and who you're looking for, sometimes it's just easier to get someone to arrange everything for you.

There are a number of tourism operators and booking agencies that offer group and tailor-made art tours around the region, either showcasing the signature spots or creating itineraries bespoke to your taste.

Among them are:

Nelson Escapes (page 65)
www.nelsonescapes.co.nz • 03 546 6338

Bay Tours
www.baytoursnelson.co.nz • 03 548 6486

Simply Wild
www.simplywild.co.nz • 03 548 8500

Executive Limousines
www.executivelimousines.co.nz • 03 545 1765

Tasman Helicopters
www.tasmanhelicopters.co.nz • 03 528 8075

Nelson Helicopters
www.nelsonhelicopters.co.nz • 03 547 1177

Nelson City Taxis
www.nelsontaxis.co.nz • 03 548 8225

Sun City Taxis
03 548 2666

Or maybe you want to rent a car:

Apex Car Rentals
www.apexrentals.co.nz • 0800 939 597

Avis Rent A Car
www.avis.co.nz • 0800 655 111

Bay Rent-A-Car
www.bayrentacar.co.nz • 0800 696 686

Hardy Cars
www.hardycars.com • 0800 903 010

Nelson Auto Rentals
www.nelsonautorentals.co.nz • 03 548 5125

New Zealand Rent A Car
www.nzrentacar.co.nz • 0800 800 956

Rent-A-Dent
www.rentadent.co.nz • 0800 736 823

Pohara looking towards Takaka. Photo: Daniel Allen

New Zealand

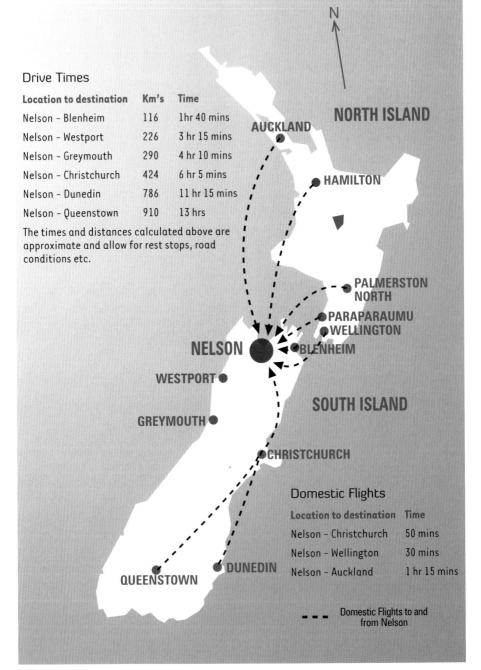

Drive Times

Location to destination	Km's	Time
Nelson – Blenheim	116	1hr 40 mins
Nelson – Westport	226	3 hr 15 mins
Nelson – Greymouth	290	4 hr 10 mins
Nelson – Christchurch	424	6 hr 5 mins
Nelson – Dunedin	786	11 hr 15 mins
Nelson – Queenstown	910	13 hrs

The times and distances calculated above are approximate and allow for rest stops, road conditions etc.

NORTH ISLAND

AUCKLAND

HAMILTON

PALMERSTON NORTH

PARAPARAUMU
WELLINGTON

NELSON   BLENHEIM

WESTPORT

SOUTH ISLAND

GREYMOUTH

CHRISTCHURCH

Domestic Flights

Location to destination	Time
Nelson – Christchurch	50 mins
Nelson – Wellington	30 mins
Nelson – Auckland	1 hr 15 mins

QUEENSTOWN   DUNEDIN

- - - Domestic Flights to and from Nelson

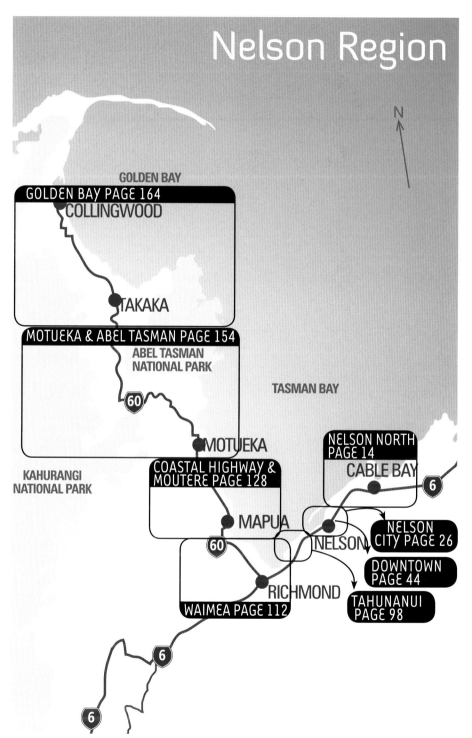

Nelson Region

N

GOLDEN BAY

GOLDEN BAY PAGE 164
COLLINGWOOD

TAKAKA

MOTUEKA & ABEL TASMAN PAGE 154

ABEL TASMAN
NATIONAL PARK

TASMAN BAY

KAHURANGI
NATIONAL PARK

60

MOTUEKA

NELSON NORTH
PAGE 14

CABLE BAY

6

COASTAL HIGHWAY &
MOUTERE PAGE 128

MAPUA

60

NELSON

NELSON
CITY PAGE 26

DOWNTOWN
PAGE 44

RICHMOND

WAIMEA PAGE 112

TAHUNANUI
PAGE 98

6

6

Nelson North

N

GLENDUAN BAY

GLEN RD

BOULDER BANK DR

6

WAKAPUA

TODD BUSH RD

SEATON STREET

BOULDER BANK

23
24

WASTNEY TERRACE

DODSON VALLEY ROAD

22

ATAWHAI DR SH6

25

ATAWHAI

ATAWHAI CRES

PORT NELSON

AKERSTEN ST

TO NELSON

29B
29A

ATAWHAI DRIVE

▼ SEE PAGE 27

CABLE
BAY

PEPIN
ISLAND

DELAWARE BAY

20 19

CABLE BAY RD

MAORI PA RD

TO BLENHEIM

WHANGAMOA ROAD SH6

CABLE BAY RD

RAYNERS RD

LUD VALLEY RD

ROSS RD

6

MAC'S RD

TEAL VALLEY RD

View across Delaware Bay. Photo: Daniel Allen

Cable Bay to Nelson

Back in the day, Cable Bay was a hub of international communications technology. In 1876 it became the terminus for the first trans-Tasman telegraph cable linking New Zealand to Australia.

Ironically for a place synonymous with communication, mobile phone coverage in Cable Bay today is practically non-existent, although I hear if you stand on top of the picnic table at the northern end of the beach you can get a weak signal.

To the right as you drive into Cable Bay is Delaware Bay - the scene of much drama in 1863 when the bay's namesake was wrecked there. The story of the crew's rescue by local Maori was the inspiration for Sally Burton's Wreck of the Delaware, one of the largest installation pieces in The Suter Art Gallery's collection, gifted by Wakatu Incorporation.

Cable Bay Café is a great example of the adage small is beautiful. Intimate, charming and decorated in gentle hues, it's a hit with the locals. The menu is loaded with good food and anyone in search of seafood won't be disappointed. When the temperature drops, customers are encouraged to take advantage of the café's cuddly collection of hot water bottles. The souvenir teaspoon and historic local photograph collection is also worthy of your attention.

Cable Bay Beach is a brilliant place to be, especially on Tuesday nights in summer. Described by one local as "A fantastic way to meet people and share a bottle of wine". Everyone, I'm told, is welcome.

Someone who knows the area better than most is furniture maker David Haig. An internationally recognised authority on steam bending and the creator of one of the world's great rocking chairs, David and his wife Clare have lived next to the estuary for 28 years.

And while David's expertise regularly sees him teaching at elite furniture schools in the USA, his love of Cable Bay remains undiminished.

"There is a magic hour that starts just as the sun is setting. It fills the bay and brings every contour of Pepin Island into sharp relief and the hills just go purple," he says.

"Anything that takes your breath away will become some source of inspiration and living here it would be hard for it not to rub off on you."

The drive from Cable Bay to Nelson is a beauty. The point where Tasman Bay comes into view, from the top of the Gentle Annie hill, is a favourite among Nelsonians. It's the sight that tells them they're home.

Opposite the Wakapuaka Hall you'll find the entrance to the Centre for Fine Woodworking and further on you'll come to the turn off to Glenduan, or as it's known locally, The Glen. If you've got the time, it's worth a visit. The stony beach provides an excellent view of Tasman Bay and the 13km long Boulder Bank, which shelters the city's harbour from rough seas, has been turning up in Nelson art since the year dot.

Wreck of the Delaware by Sally Burton (above). Photo: The Suter Art Gallery. The Boulder Bank and Lighthouse. Photo: Nelson Tasman Tourism

David Haig
Furniture Maker

796 Cable Bay Road • Nelson • 03 545 0455
haig@clear.net.nz • www.davidhaigfurniture.com

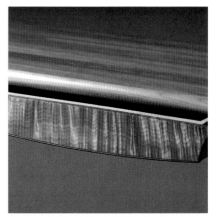

David has worked full time as a furniture designer and maker for the past 25 years.

His multiple award-winning Signature rocking chair has become a design classic, and features in homes and collections around the world. He works from his home on the edge of the Wakapuaka Estuary in Cable Bay - just a short walk from the beach.

David says it's an idyllic and inspiring place to work and the magic of living there has never dulled. His ongoing passion is exploring ways to incorporate bold curving forms in solid wood, whilst retaining the respect for materials and function demanded of fine contemporary furniture designers. He teaches regularly in the U.S. and is a co-tutor at Nelson's own Centre for Fine Woodworking.

Visitors please ring first. Commissions welcomed.

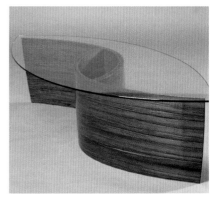

Cable Bay Café

799 Cable Bay Rd • Cable Bay • 03 546 8799
cablebaycafe@xtra.co.nz

The delightful little Cable Bay Café offers fresh seafood, local produce and wines with views of the estuary and Pepin Island. Features include an outdoor courtyard and a kiddies sandpit.

On the left at Cable Bay, next to the motor camp.

Kay Field at Cable Bay Cafe (above, left). Photo: Nelson Mail. Tasman Bay from Gentle Annie (above, right). View from Cable Bay (below)

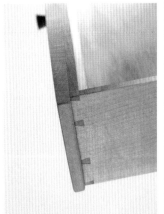
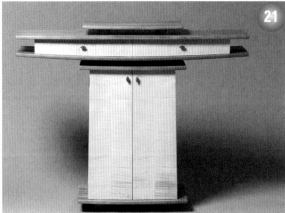

John Shaw - Furniture Maker

The Centre for Fine Woodworking
Main Road • Wakapuaka • RD1 Nelson
03 545 2674 day • 03 548 8793 a/h
027 635 3641
john@johnshawfurnituremaker.co.nz
www.johnshawfurnituremaker.co.nz
www.cfw.co.nz

John has been a furniture maker for over 25 years. He presently divides his time between fulfilling commissions and tutoring at the Centre for Fine Woodworking.

Superbly constructed, John's designs are always a pleasure to live with.

Boulder Bank & Lighthouse (below). Photo: Nelson Tasman Tourism

Nigel Whitton of NW Designs

135 Dodson Valley Rd • Atawhai
Nelson • 021 723 619
nigel@nwdesigns.co.nz
www.nwdesigns.co.nz

"All true artists, whether they know it
or not, create from a place of
no-mind, from inner stillness."
- Eckhart Tolle

Nigel Whitton of NW Designs is a
designer and craftsman of fine
furniture as well as a traditionally
trained shipwright and boat builder.
He divides his time between private
furniture commissions, tutoring at
the Centre for Fine Woodworking and
international super yacht interior
refit contracts.

Visits by appointment please.

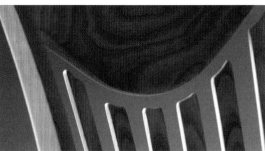

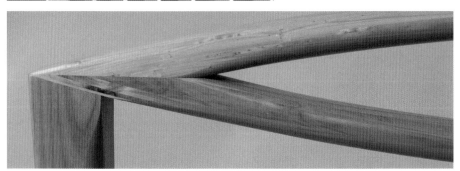

Adrian Myers

Natures Jewels

Atawhai • Nelson • 03 545 2052
027 335 6052
adrianmyers@naturesjewels.co.nz
www.naturesjewels.co.nz

Adrian Myers creates quality jewellery inspired by his love of the wild flowers and foliage of New Zealand and other countries. Working with a wide range of materials including 18 carat and other gold alloys, precious and semi-precious stones, greenstone, mother-of-pearl, hardwoods and enamel, Adrian's work captures the essence of wild flora.

Commissions welcomed, visits by appointment only.
Price range: $200 - $6,000.

Outlets: ROC's, Richmond; Hanne Andersen, Wellington; Agosy Jewellery, Christchurch.

Tony Allain

28 Tresillian Avenue • Atawhai • Nelson
03 545 1264 • tony.allain@yahoo.co.nz

With an eye for subtle beauty, Tony works and paints in the tradition of an impressionist artist creating pieces filled with colour and light.

Outlets: Flagstaff Gallery, Auckland; Statements Gallery, Napier; Exhibitions Gallery of Fine Arts, Wellington.

Studio/Gallery: Open most days from 11am.

View over Tasman Bay to the Western Ranges (below). Photo: Daniel Allen

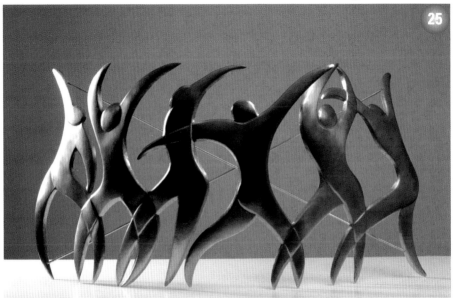

Ken Laws

470 Atawhai Drive • Atawhai • Nelson • 03 545 0868
ka.laws@xtra.co.nz

Ken achieves an original form of expression by sculpting in the unusual medium of stainless steel. Although steel might be considered a hard and cold material, the reflections and depth that Ken imbues give his eye-catching works a softer, far more subtle, transient, warm and personal feel.

Outlets: WOW®, Nelson ; Fishers Fine Arts, Christchurch; Exhibitions Gallery, Wellington; Central Art, Queenstown; Oriel Gallery, Picton.

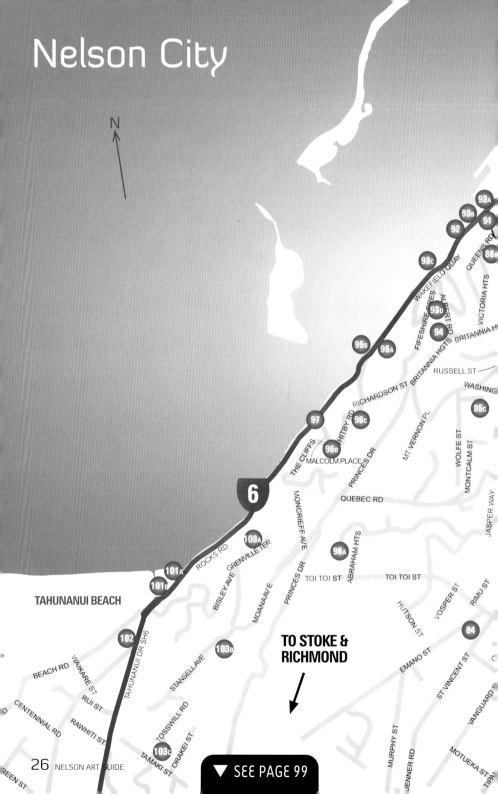

Nelson City

N

▼ SEE PAGE 99

TAHUNANUI BEACH

TO STOKE &
RICHMOND

6

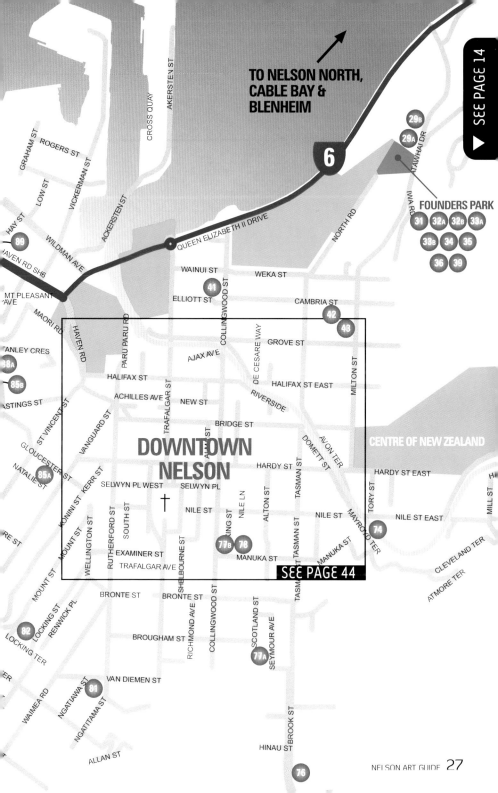

TO NELSON NORTH, CABLE BAY & BLENHEIM

6

GRAHAM ST
ROGERS ST
LOW ST
HAY ST
VICKERMAN ST
AKERSTEN ST
CROSS QUAY

WILDMAN AVE
HAVEN RD SH6
89

MAORI RD
MT PLEASANT AVE

QUEEN ELIZABETH II DRIVE
NORTH RD

WAINUI ST
WEKA ST

29B
29A
ATAWHAI DR
IWA RD

FOUNDERS PARK
31 32A 32B 33A
38B 34 35
36 39

WAINUI ST
41
ELLIOTT ST
COLLINGWOOD ST
CAMBRIA ST
42
43

HANLEY CRES
38A
85B
HASTINGS ST

HAVEN RD
PARU PARU RD
AJAX AVE
DE CESARE WAY
GROVE ST
MILTON ST

HALIFAX ST
ACHILLES AVE
TRAFALGAR ST
NEW ST
RIVERSIDE
HALIFAX ST EAST

BRIDGE ST
AVON TER

ST VINCENT ST
VANGUARD ST
ALMA LN
DOWNTOWN NELSON
HARDY ST
TASMAN ST
DOMETT ST
CENTRE OF NEW ZEALAND
HARDY ST EAST

GLOUCESTER ST
NATALIE ST
85A
KONINI ST
KERR ST
SELWYN PL WEST
SELWYN PL
NILE ST
NILE LN
ALTON ST
TASMAN ST
NILE ST
TORY ST
HARDY ST EAST
MILL ST
NILE ST EAST

MOUNT ST
RUTHERFORD ST
SOUTH ST
KING ST
77B 78
MANUKA ST
MAYROAD TER
74
CLEVELAND TER
ATMORE TER

WELLINGTON ST
EXAMINER ST
SHELBOURNE ST
TRAFALGAR AVE
SEE PAGE 44

BRONTE ST
BRONTE ST
COLLINGWOOD ST
RICHMOND AVE
SCOTLAND ST
SEYMOUR AVE

LOCKING PL
RENWICK PL
82
LOCKING TER
BROUGHAM ST
77A
BROOK ST

VAN DIEMEN ST
81
NGATIAWA ST
NGATITAMA ST
WAIMEA RD

ALLAN ST
HINAU ST
76

Founders Heritage Park Windmill. Photo: Nelson Mail

Founders Heritage Park & The Wood

If boutique beer, buildings from a bygone era, artists, cheeky ducks, train rides, fresh baking and curious pukeko sound like your idea of fun, you need to put Founders Heritage Park near the top of your 'to do' list while visiting Nelson.

As you enter the park through the windmill you'll see to your right a gorgeous old house featuring a lead light window bearing the name Duncan. The house belonged to brewer Henry Duncan and originally sat near the corner of Hardy and Domett Streets in the central city.

Today, Henry's grandson John Duncan is a fifth generation Nelson brewer and operates the award-winning park brewery, Founders Brewery - the the first in Australasia to be certified organic.

The brewery café is one of Nelson's best spots for meeting people and whiling away an afternoon. The place goes off in summer, especially on Friday nights, when the Duncans let punters bring their own takeaways for dinner. Friday night is also a good time to visit Nelson's Farmers' Market, where you'll find everything from cacti to great value organic salad mix.

Behind the brewery there is a good playground, a working railway and an old plane that could have come out of an Indiana Jones movie. In short: the kids will love it.

Featuring a mix of old, new and replica buildings, the spacious park is the scene of the annual Founders Book Fair every June.

What Woodstock did for music, the Founders Book Fair does for second hand books. Each year thousands of bibliophiles of all ages, including dealers from around the country, charge into the park to snap up hundreds of thousands of donated titles for bargain prices. The money goes toward upkeep of the park.

Founders also has an increasing number of artists in residence.

Te Whare Tupuna Kaakati

Whakatu Marae

99 Atawhai Drive • Nelson • 03 546 9097
kaiawhina@whakatumarae.co.nz

Kaupapa Māori - we provide facilities for noho marae (stay over), conferences, promotional events and cultural visits.

Whakamanatia te tapu, te ihi, te wehi o te whanāu — to address, restore and enhance the mana and tapu of the whanāu.

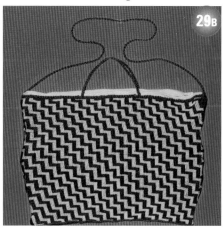

Marlin Elkington

Toi Taniko Art • F5/121 Atawhai Drive • Nelson
027 274 4927 • twmmarlin@hotmail.com

'Taniko Art' traditional Māori taniko weaving techniques with a modern approach, Marlin creates kete and accessories to adorn the body and interiors.

Founders Heritage Park (below). Photo: Nelson Mail

Miyazu Gardens, Atawhai Drive. Photo: Nelson Mail

31

Founders Heritage Park

87 Atawhai Drive • Nelson • 03 548 2649
www.founderspark.co.nz

A Nelson City Council community and visitor attaction.

Stroll through the character streets, village greens and tranquil established gardens of Founders Heritage Park and experience life as it was in Nelson from the 1880s to the 1930s. Founders hosts the weekly Farmers Market from 3pm - 6pm every Friday evening as well as quarterly Nelson Beer Fetes, MarchFest, the Festival of Opportunities, Antique to Retro Extravaganza, Queen's Birthday Book Fair and many more popular events.

See www.founderspark.co.nz for details.

Open: Daily from 10am - 4.30pm.

Founders Brewery & Café

Founders Heritage Park • 87 Atawhai Drive • Nelson
03 548 4638 • foundersbrewery@xtra.co.nz
www.biobrew.co.nz

Founders Brewery is the home of premium, organic, hand-crafted beers brewed on location. Taste the award-winning Tall Blonde, Long Black, Red Head, Generation and seasonal beers. Brewery tours and beer tastings available. The café style menu features local and organic food in a family-friendly setting.

Open: Daily, all year 10am - 4.30pm, Fri until dusk.

L'Artisan Bread

The Art of Bread • Founders Heritage Park
87 Atawhai Drive • Nelson • 03 539 0009
bread@ts.co.nz

L'Artisan create handmade breads and pastries true to the European artisan baker's tradition using fresh, mostly organic, local ingredients. Their secret is unhurried fermentation for better flavour and texture. You'll also find L'Artisan at Nelson's Saturday Market.

Open: Tues 10am - 2pm, Fri 3pm - 6pm.

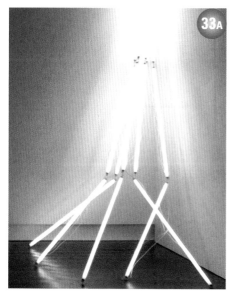

33A

33B

Photo (top): Daniel Allen

Andy Clover

Founders Heritage Park • 87 Atawhai Drive • Nelson
021 478 651 • info@andyclover.com
www.andyclover.com

Andy's practice ranges across experimental sculptural work, photography, drawing and installations involving vinyl graphics, acrylic media and electronic lights. Pieces often utilise found and converted objects and elements of text or graffiti for content. Architectural and site-specific commissions welcome.

Visit by appointment only.

Tim Royall

Founders Heritage Park • 87 Atawhai Drive • Nelson
03 539 0377 • 021 150 5214 • timroyall@xtra.co.nz

Tim's work in both sculpture and jewellery with stone, his preferred material, is based on the rhythms and structures of nature. His pieces are attracting wide attention for their elegant lines and essential forms. Courses available. Commissions welcomed. Visits by appointment.

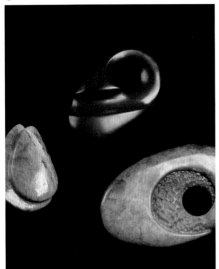

34

Ian Longley

Concepts in Stone, Jewellery and Jade Carving • Founders Heritage Park
87 Atawhai Drive • Nelson • 03 548 2901
027 687 0072 • longley@xtra.co.nz

From his studio in the tranquil setting of Founders Heritage Park, Ian creates beautiful and unique jewellery, carvings and small sculptures. His inspiration comes from NZ stone, and his sensitive work highlights the colours and patterns that are inherent in each piece. He specialises in commission work, and loves the collaboration involved in bringing each idea into a tangible form.

Open: Tues to Fri 10am – 4pm or by appointment.

35

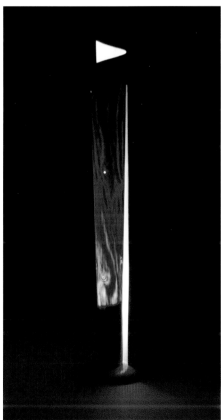

Roger Davies

Furniture

Roger Davies Furniture • Siding Workshop, Founders
Heritage Park • 87 Atawhai Drive • Nelson
03 546 9399 • 027 444 7831 • rogerfurniture@xtra.co.nz

A meticulous craftsman joiner and fine furniture maker, Roger combines his craft traditions with original ideas and contemporary technological innovations. Some of his creations are simple elegant reconstructions of objects from a bygone era, while others are beautiful designs for the modern age. Whether in the form of a handcrafted bathroom cabinet or a steam-bent, vacuum-moulded chair, Davies' work expresses his dedication to the integrity of his materials and a reliable, functional aesthetic.

View by appointment.

Mantis Workshop

John Sharples & Jo Ellis

Founders Heritage Park • 87 Atawhai Drive • Nelson
03 548 6526 • 021 078 6386
john@mantisworkshop.com • www.mantisworkshop.com

Mantis workshop creates beautiful and practical pots, gates and art objects. John and Jo work from both home and Founders Heritage Park. Life has now allowed them time to be creative, and their main requisite is to have fun doing it. You can also find their work at the Nelson Saturday Market.

FARMERS @ Founders

NELSON PROVINCIAL FARMERS MARKET INC.

MARKET DAY
Every FRIDAY
3pm-6.00pm
Free Admission

Stall at the Farmers Market , Farmers Market Sign, Founders Book Fair and Festival of Opportunities (left to right, top to bottom). Photos: Nelson Mail

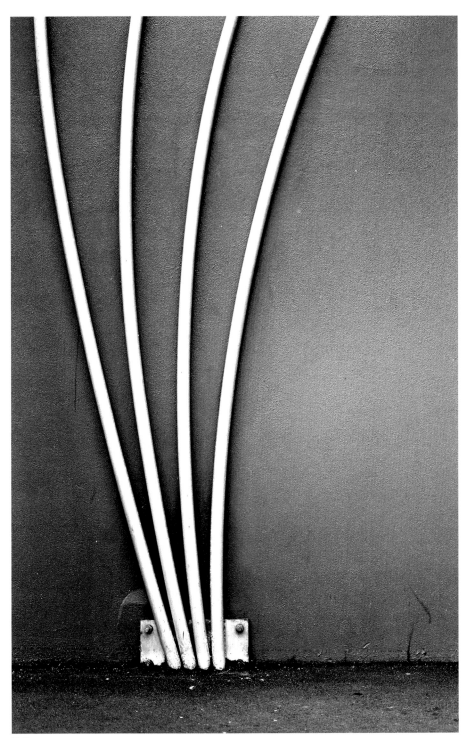

Daniel Allen
Photography

PO Box 1197 • Nelson • 03 545 6135 • 021 049 0827
studio@danielallen.co.nz • www.danielallen.co.nz

Daniel Allen got his first camera at seven,
enrolled in a camera club at ten, built his first
dark room at eleven and has been passionate
about photography ever since.

Originally from London, Daniel moved to Nelson
in 2003 and quickly established himself as one
of the South Island's leading photographers.

From his base in Nelson, Daniel covers New
Zealand for a diverse range of advertising,
editorial and publishing clients.

Anne Rush Artworks

29 Elliott Street • Nelson • 03 545 9390 • 021 220 7441
annerush@orcon.net.nz

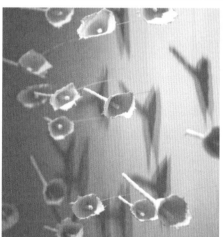

Anne Rush is one of Nelson's most celebrated mixed-media artists and local art guides. From her home studio in one of Nelson's heritage streets, Anne hand-builds 'sculptured paintings' to the size and scale of each specific site, be it residential or commercial.

The central inspiration of her work is the Arum Lily, which Anne uses to explore the relationship between shadow and light, memory and experience and the emotional transitions in our lives.

Meanwhile, Anne's personalised art tours explore the essence of the region's spectacular scenery and unique culture through the lives and work of local artists.

Commission enquiries are welcome. Visit by appointment. Price range: $200 - $8,000.

42

Maria Middlebrook-Wells

Dip V.A.

MJMW Arts • 60A Cambria Street • Nelson
03 548 3793 • 027 548 3793 • mjmw@xtra.co.nz
www.nelsonartists.co.nz

Maria's landscapes draw on Pacific influences
and reflect her childhood spent in a port
town in the shadow of Mt Taranaki. She is a
contemporary artist who paints in oils and
experiments with a wide variety of mixed
media including collage on canvas and
furniture. Maria also enjoys creating public
artwork — she has completed mosaics in
Pioneer Park and the Nelson Hospital grounds.

Visit by appointment and layby welcome.

43

The Sprig & Fern Tavern

Tasman Brewing Company

134 Milton Street • Nelson • 03 545 7117
www.sprigandfern.co.nz • tasmanbrewing@tasman.net

Old values, not old fashioned... The Sprig & Fern Tavern is fast becoming a local icon in The Wood area. There are 15 locally brewed beers on tap, all 100% natural with no additives, no pokie machines, no pool tables and no televisions blaring, so customers can actually talk to one another.

Open: Daily 10am – 10pm.

The Sprig & Fern Tavern (below). Photo: Daniel Allen

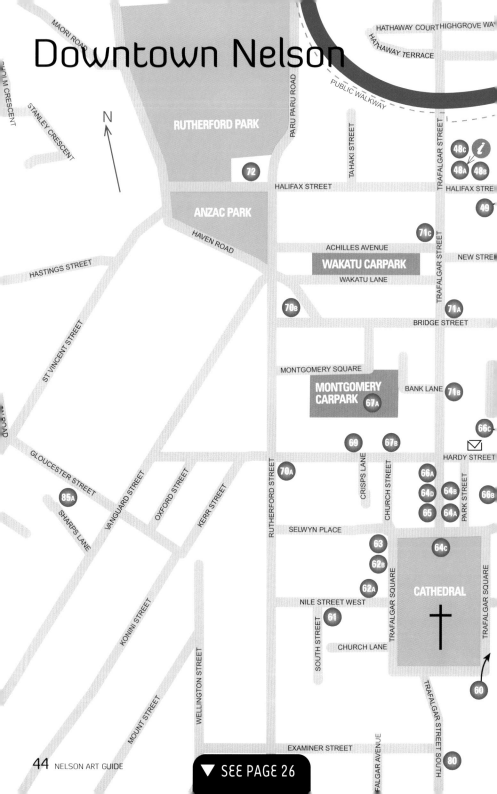

Downtown Nelson

▼ SEE PAGE 26

▲ SEE PAGE 27

DI LEVA WAY
MONOPOLI WAY
ROSA CRISTINA WAY
BELLA GROVE WAY
JENVILLE WAY
DAYMAN WAY
MAHITAHI WAY
ALBANO WAY
GROVE STREET
KOTUKU WAY
SHAKESPEARE WALK

50
51

PUBLIC WALKWAY

LANCEWOOD WAY **TO NELSON
NORTH, CABLE BAY
& BLENHEIM**

RIVERSIDE

PETTIT PLACE

HALIFAX STREET EAST

TASMAN STREET

MILTON STREET

MAITAI RIVER

MALTHOUSE LANE

PROVINCIAL LANE

NGAIRE LANE

52A 52B

COLLINGWOOD STREET

HARLEY STREET

55

53B

52C

OLDHAM LANE

ST JOHN STREET   **POLICE**

**QUEENS
GARDENS**

73

AVON TERRACE

**CENTP
OF NZ**

TASMAN STREET

HARDY STREET

**NELSON MARLBOROUGH
INSTITUTE OF TECHNOLOGY**

ALTON STREET

ALTON LANE

BARRINGTON WAY

DOMETT STREET

NILE AVENUE

57

SCHOOL OF MUSIC LANE

COLLINGWOOD STREET

59

53A

NILE STREET

MAYROYD TL

KING STREET

HARPER STREET

75

77B 78

CLEVELAND TERRACE

MANUKA STREET

▼ SEE PAGE 27

Downtown Nelson

For a city with a population of only 45,000, central Nelson is a pretty remarkable place.

How many other cities that size boast a museum, an art gallery, a world class market, a music school, a nine-screen cinema complex inside a beautiful art deco building, a glass blowing studio, a Japanese calligraphy studio and corrugated iron cabbage trees?

Downtown Nelson is easy to get around, full of good places to eat and drink, and you're never far from a lovely park or the Maitai River.

Architecturally there is plenty on offer; from the elegance of Lambretta's Café on Hardy Street and the classical lines of The Vic Mac's Brewbar at the top end of Trafalgar Street, to the modern stylings of

the Miller's Acre Centre at the lower end of the street.

Enough old buildings remain intact to give you an idea of where Nelson has been, and a growing number of thoughtfully designed new ones suggest where it might be heading. Scattered among them you will find dealer galleries, fashion designers, cafés, restaurants and public artworks.

The artworks range in scale from Bruce Mitchell's immense Southern Cross carved from seven tonnes of Golden Bay black marble, to a life size bust of café pioneer Eelco Boswijk by Siene de Vries, both on Trafalgar Street.

Personal favourites include Jeff Thomson's aforementioned Cabbage Trees (ti rakau) in the walkway between Trafalgar Street and Wakatu Square, Gavin Hitchings' smooth stainless steel Vessel on the Miller's Acre Centre and Tim Wraight's beautifully carved panels, also at the centre.

Upper Trafalgar Street (above). Photo: Grant Stirling

Opposite page: (top left, clockwise) Catchment Gallery, Glass blowing at Flamedaisy, Nelson Market, Local Art Market, Cocktail at Harry's Bar and sushi at the Oyster Bar

Vessel

Vessel is the sculpture on the face of Millers Acre Centre, Taha o te Awa. The stainless steel piece was designed by Nelson jeweller and sculptor Gavin Hitchings in reference to Nelson's maritime heritage.

Nelson i-SITE Visitor Centre

Millers Acre Centre • Cnr Trafalgar & Halifax Sts
Nelson • 03 548 2304 • fax 03 546 7393
Nelson@i-SITE.org • www.NelsonNZ.com

Nelson i-SITE puts you in the picture.

While you're in Nelson, come and talk to our knowledgeable staff. We'll make bookings for you and offer friendly, objective advice on things to see and do nearby and nationwide, including activities, attractions, accommodation and transport bookings.

Reef Knot

Reef Knot is by Nelson sculptor Grant Palliser. Two strands of steel form a nautical knot that symbolically links history and present day.

Rutherford Gallery

42 Halifax Street • Nelson • 03 548 1878
021 151 3968 • suetaylor@rutherfordgallery.co.nz

The Rutherford Gallery is Nelson's oldest
and largest dealer gallery housing a
collection of contemporary paintings by
locally and nationally recognised artists.
Picture framing a specialty.

Open: Mon to Fri 8.30am - 5.30pm, Sat
(Summer) 9.30am - 4pm and Sat (Winter)
10am - 1pm.

50

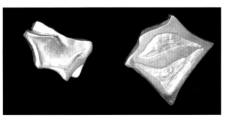

Sue Bateup – Maitai Gallery

(Incorporating Weavers Gallery)

15B Ajax Avenue • Nelson • 03 545 7080 • 021 030 6698
sue@suebateup.co.nz • www.suebateup.co.nz

Sue Bateup creates art and wearable designs from her studio overlooking the tranquil Maitai River in central Nelson, just two minutes walk along the river from the Nelson i-SITE Visitor Centre.

Sue has been crafting her hand-woven and hand-knitted garments and accessories for 18 years and recently expanded her practise to include jewellery, sculpture, painting and photography.

Open: Weekdays. Price range: $40 - $360.

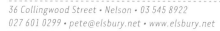

Lustre Gallery

36 Collingwood Street • Nelson • 03 545 8922
027 601 0299 • pete@elsbury.net • www.elsbury.net

Visit this riverside gallery and experience the work of some of Nelson's leading contemporary jewellers. Artists in residence include owners Peter Elsbury and Zoe Buchanan. Purchase a piece from their unique range or talk to the makers about a commissioned original.

Lustre also displays work from local painters and sculptors.

You are most welcome to call in.
Open: Mon to Fri 9am – 5pm and Sat 11am – 3pm.

Top of Trafalgar

52B

High Flyers

High Flyers, created by Grant Palliser as a city millennium commission is a kinetic sculpture that responds to the energy of the rapids in the Maitai River. Its five polished stainless steel poles reflect the tones of the environment, while the aluminium 'boulders' echo the river stones, symbolising opportunities, goals and achievements in the 'river of life'.

Ann Nighy Cards & Things

DipHSc., Dip Teach., Cert VisArts

1/227 Bridge Street • Nelson • 03 548 4358
027 255 5046 • ann.nighy@xtra.co.nz
www.annnighyartandcards.vpweb.com

Ann has a quirky sense of humour. She is a versatile artist who works quickly, producing images in watercolour, acrylic, pen, ink and pastel on paper and canvas. Ann creates general and Nelson-specific greeting cards and stunning brooches. Commissions welcome.

To the Towers

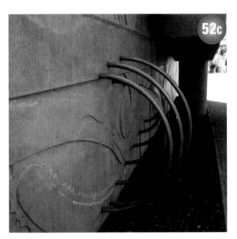

52C

Located opposite The Suter Art Gallery, hours variable. Most works priced under $200.

Aratuna Normanby Bridge

Aratuna Normanby Bridge is the new bridge across the Maitai River. Aratuna means 'pathway of eels' and the bridge boasts tactile art by Brian Flintoff and Grant Palliser, in the form of sinuous eels writhing into a kowhaiwhai pattern and escaping from the stylised hinake (eel trap).

53A

53B

Lori Davis Paintings

117 Nile Street • Nelson • 03 545 7510 • 027 488 6887
lori@loridavis.co.nz • www.loridavis.co.nz

In her gallery next to the Global Soap Company Lori paints vivid, original works on quality Waterford paper. Prints and cards are also available. Price range: $150 – $1,500.

Open: Mon to Fri 11am – 5pm or by appointment.

Sentinel

Sentinel sails in the Queens Gardens pond. It is inspired by the base of the Nikau palm frond and refers to the waka and ships which brought waves of people to New Zealand. Created by Dominique de Borrekens and Grant Scott.

Sculpture by Jim McKay, outside The Suter Art Gallery (below). Photo: The Suter Art Gallery

55

The Suter Art Gallery
Te Aratoi o Whakatū

208 Bridge Street • Nelson • 03 548 4699 • fax 03 548 1236
info@thesuter.org.nz • www.thesuter.org.nz

The Suter Te Aratoi o Whakatu is the public art gallery for the Nelson region. Its vision is reflected in the Maori name given to The Suter: 'Te Aratoi o Whakatu – Art is the Pathway for Whakatu, Nelson'.

Established in 1899, it is one of New Zealand's oldest art galleries and also includes a theatre, café and store featuring local artists' works. The Suter has a significant collection of art and presents a dynamic programme of exhibitions, events and education services.
From the local to the international, there is something for all ages and interests.

Open: Daily 10.30am - 4.30pm.
$3 Adults, 50c Children, $1 Students with ID. Free entry on Saturday.
Closed Christmas Day, New Year's Day and Good Friday.

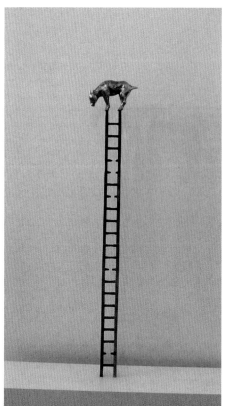

Nelson Marlborough Institute of Technology

Fishbowl Gallery

322 Hardy Street • Nelson • 0800 4 CAREER , 0800 422 733
info@nmit.ac.nz • www.nmit.ac.nz

NMIT's School of Arts and Media and the Nelson School of Music play a leading role in the region's arts and media education and make a major contribution to the current strength and vibrancy of the Top of the South arts sector. NMIT offers certificate, diploma, degree and post graduate level study in Arts and Media. Many successful artists, musicians, writers and designers are graduates from these programmes and are working in key roles in the arts and media fields.

Check out the latest works from NMIT's students, graduates and tutors at NMIT's Fishbowl Gallery, ground floor, Library Learning Centre, Alton Street, Nelson.

Fishbowl Gallery Open: Mid Feb to End of Nov - Mon to Thurs 8am - 8pm, Fri 8am - 6pm and Sat 9am - 12pm. Summer break, (Early Dec to mid Feb) Mon to Fri 8.30am - 5pm.

South Street. Photo: Daniel Allen

South Street & Cathedral Area

To get an idea of what Nelson was once like, take a stroll down historic South Street. Nelson's best preserved street may look like a museum piece but it's still home to a few locals.

Heritage buildings can be found scattered throughout central Nelson and are an important part of the city's fabric. Keep an eye out for The Nelson Club, a striking piece of real estate in Selwyn Place. Nearby you'll also find the remarkable Tula and Niles which sells vintage clothing and collectables in an elegant old villa.

From here, head along upper Nile Street to the Nelson School of Music. One of the country's oldest music institutions, the school was founded in 1894. If you get a chance, have a look in the auditorium. Opened in 1901, it's a favourite with touring acts for its excellent acoustics and beautiful interior. The auditorium is also the main venue for the school's annual Winter Festival, which in recent years has featured everyone from dDub to Flight of the Conchords.

Nearby from Church Hill, the Christ Church Cathedral overlooks the city business district. Built mainly of Takaka marble, the cathedral is open to visitors, and interpretation panels tell more of its history.

Photo: Mark Holmes

Nelson School of Music

48 Nile Street • Nelson • 03 548 9477
nsom@nsom.ac.nz • www.nsom.ac.nz

This historic auditorium is renowned for its excellent acoustics, and is a preferred concert venue and facility for quality events, music and education.

Contact us for current performances.

dDub (below). Photo: Nelson School of Music.
View of South Street (right). Photo: Daniel Allen

Photos: Grant Stirling

Consulate Apartments

353 Trafalgar Square • Nelson • 03 545 8200 • 027 437 4041 • fax 03 548 4156
consulate@consulateapartments.co.nz • www.consulateapartments.co.nz

Overlooking the stately Nelson Cathedral grounds are the exclusive Consulate Apartments. Three elegant, self-contained, serviced suites offer private luxury accommodation a short stroll from Nelson's central city restaurants and cafés, art galleries, regional museum and the Nelson School of Music.

Celebrating Nelson's creativity, each apartment showcases local artists' work, beautifully complementing the opulent interior design. Personalised art tours can also be arranged to gain unique insight into Nelson's art culture.

61

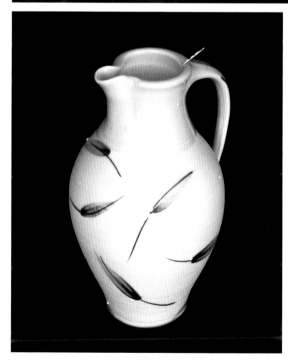

South Street Gallery

10 Nile Street • Nelson • 03 548 8117
southst@clear.net.nz
www.nelsonpottery.co.nz

South Street Gallery houses modern and traditional ceramics from 25 selected artists of national and international renown.

Downstairs – all works made in Nelson. Upstairs – work from the West Coast.

Worldwide postage (fully insured). All major credit cards and EFTPOS accepted.

Open: Mon to Fri 9am - 5pm, Sat 9am - 4pm and Sun 10am - 4pm.

62A

62B

Flamedaisy Glass Design

324 Trafalgar Square • Nelson • 03 548 4475
flamedaisy@clear.net.nz • www.flamedaisy.com

Flamedaisy is the boutique glassblowing studio of Anthony and Berinthia Genet where you can watch the magic of art glass blowing and try it yourself.

Open: Mon to Fri 10am – 5pm, weekends 10am – 4pm or by appointment (closed Sun during Winter).

Rutherford Hotel Nelson

A Heritage Hotel

Cnr of Trafalgar Square and Nile Street West • Nelson
03 548 2299 • fax 03 546 3003
enquiries@rutherfordhotel.co.nz
www.rutherfordhotel.co.nz

Within walking distance to the city centre Rutherford Hotel Nelson – A Heritage Hotel, offers a mix of cosmopolitan sophistication and local charm. The hotel includes studio rooms and suites with a range of facilities to ensure your stay is memorable.

Jens Hansen Gold & Silversmith

Cnr of Trafalgar Square and Selwyn Place • Nelson
03 548 0640 • 021 299 3380 • info@jenshansen.com
www.jenshansen.com

Born from one man's passion and individuality, Jens Hansen is internationally recognised for classically designed jewellery with true spirit and timeless style. Handcrafted jewellery originals in gold and silver can only be seen at the Nelson studio workshop, where there is a spectacular selection of signature rings and accompanying pieces. We can also handcraft your own unique ring, as we did for the Lord of the Rings movie trilogy.

Open: Mon to Fri 9am - 5pm, Sat 9am-2pm.
Summer open: Sun 10am - 1pm.

Eelco Bust

The bronze bust of prominent Nelsonian, Eelco Boswijk, by Siene de Vries, looks out from the former 'Chez Eelco'café (now House of Ales). Established in 1961, the Chez Eelco was a Nelson institution and reputedly the oldest café in New Zealand.

Symonds Gas Lamp

The Symonds Gas Lamp is a replica of the original, which was erected in 1880's at the intersection of Hardy and Trafalgar Streets as a memorial to leading local merchant John Symonds. The replica was a Nelson 150th celebration project erected in 1992, based on enlarged photographs of the original.

Church Steps

Designed by Arthur Reynolds Griffin (1884 - 1967), the church steps were installed in 1913 to replace wooden steps that had become unsafe. They were made from granite quarried from Tonga Bay (now part of Abel Tasman National Park) with funding from local benefactor Thomas Cawthron.

Fibre Spectrum

280 Trafalgar Street • Nelson • 03 548 1939
info@fibrespectrum.co.nz • www.fibrespectrum.co.nz

Visit the Fibre Spectrum shop near the Cathedral steps, meet local fibre artists and view an amazing variety of their crafts.
Open: Sep/Apr weekdays 9am - 5.30pm.
May/Aug weekdays 9am - 5pm. Sat 9.30am - 2pm.

65

Nelson Escapes
Tourism Agency

284 Trafalgar Street • Nelson • 03 546 6331 (opt 1)
info@nelsonescapes.co.nz • www.nelsonescapes.co.nz

Nelson Escapes Tourism Agency is a fresh, vibrant tourism and booking agency located at the top of Trafalgar Street, nestled amongst restaurants, cafés and Nelsons iconic church steps. Our local knowledge and experience can help you create your own specialised Nelson Art Escape, choose from do-it-yourself trails to exclusive driven tours.

Feel free to contact us or pop into our office on Nelson's main street.

The Nelson Provincial Museum

Pupuri Taonga O Te Tai Ao

Cnr Hardy & Trafalgar Streets • Nelson • 03 548 9588 or 03 547 9740 • www.nelsonmuseum.co.nz

The museum collection holds a diverse range of natural and social history items with links to the past of the Nelson and Tasman region. A variety of exhibitions create a stimulating and enjoyable experience for visitors.

Open: Daily from 10am. Phone 03 548 9588 for information or 03 547 9740 for research enquiries.

Morrison Street Café

244 Hardy Street • Nelson • 03 548 8110 mail@morrisonstreetcafe.co.nz www.morrisonstreetcafe.co.nz

A stylish central city café with seriously good food, local art on the walls, outdoor seating and lots of dietary options.

Located on the corner of Hardy and Morrison Streets.

Catchment Gallery

255 Hardy Street • Nelson • 03 539 4100 021 158 1973 • catchment@paradise.net.nz www.catchment.co.nz

Catchment Gallery is situated in Nelson's rapidly growing café and fashion district. The gallery is in its fifth year and has a great depth of high quality artworks from New Zealand artists - contemporary paintings, fine art prints, sculpture and jewellery. Exhibitions change monthly.

Open: Tues to Fri 10am - 5pm, Sat 11am - 3pm.

Betts Art Supplies

153 Hardy Street • Nelson • 03 548 4276
bettsart@ihug.co.nz

Fine art and graphics supplies plus amazing papers.

Open: Mon to Fri 9am - 5.30pm, Sat 9am - 2 pm.

Artist Fiona Sutherland at the Art Market. Photo: Maria Bennich

Photo: N Knight

Nelson Markets

Montgomery Square • Nelson • 03 546 6454
www.nelsonmarket.co.nz

Experience the bustling Nelson Saturday Market. Over 100 stalls with art, crafts, jewellery, fashion, fresh fruit, veges, breads, cheeses and organic produce, plants and 'Everything under the sun!'

At Monty's Sunday Market, fossick for treasures amongst with recycled goods, pre-loved clothing, household items, bric-a-brac and other variety stalls.

Open: Sat and Sun, 8am - 1pm.

Above (L to R): From '19 Words For Now': Yume – Dream; Ikiru – Alive; Ku – Air; Warau – Laugh. Now in Private Collections in Dublin, Ireland; Langkawi, Malaysia; Banks Peninsula, New Zealand; Tokyo, Japan. Below: Yama – Mountain; Private Collection, Arnhem, The Netherlands.

All 355mm x 1670mm, sumi and acrylic on canvas.

Opposite (Top): Tim & Akiko Crowther with Uyamau – Respect. Calligraphy by Akiko, silk scroll by her Mother, Mitsue Yamagata (age 88). (Centre) L: Ai – Love. Sumi on canvas. R: Ro Nyaku – Old, Young. Sumi on Takaka Marble. (Below): Kakizome Highest Honour winner, Yousif Cahusac de Caux (age 8) with his work Hinode – Sunrise. Photo: Elspeth Collier. All others: Daniel Allen

Yū Yū

Japanese Calligraphy Gallery &
School

129 Hardy Street • Nelson • 03 545 7487
tim@yuyu.co.nz • www.yuyu.co.nz

Yū Yū is New Zealand's first Japanese calligraphy gallery and
school, owned by Japanese Master Calligrapher, Akiko Crowther,
and her husband Tim. In their serene and beautiful space (Yū Yū
means calm, peaceful and eternal) Akiko creates and teaches
traditional calligraphy. Together, Akiko and Tim also make
unique, meaningful works of modern calligraphy on canvas, and
many smaller pieces with the simplicity, elegance and strength
of one word.

In 2008, Akiko's young Nelson students won the 'Tokusen'
Highest Honour, and 4 Gold, 5 Silver, and 15 Bronze Awards at
the prestigious Kakizome Competition in Japan.

Commissions are welcomed. Open: Tues to Sat, 10am - 5pm.

70A

Pomeroy's Coffee & Tea Co

80 Hardy Street • Nelson • 03 546 6944
sales@pomeroys.co.nz
www.pomeroys.co.nz

There is an art to creating the perfect coffee and for 19 years Pomeroy's has been roasting the finest beans fresh every day. Experience the unique atmosphere of the city store, or the Coffee Factory & Cafe.

City Store; Open: Mon to Fri 9am – 5pm. Sat 9.30am – 12.30pm. The Coffee Factory; (18 Elms Street, Wakatu Industrial Estate, Stoke) Open: Mon to Fri 8.30am – 4.30pm.

Brent Forbes
TIME OF DAY

70B

RED
ART GALLERY

RED

RED Art Gallery

1 Bridge Street • Nelson • 03 548 2170
redgallery@clear.net.nz • www.redartgallery.com

RED is housed in one of Nelson's oldest buildings. Charming, unique, stylish and a must visit when in Nelson, RED has a lively exhibition programme representing New Zealand artists.

The gallery also has a great little café with fantastic coffee.

Open: Mon to Fri 9.30am – 4pm. Summer, Sat 10am – 2pm.

Southern Cross

Southern Cross was created by Takaka Hill sculptor Bruce Mitchell in 1992 from seven tonnes of Golden Bay black marble. Based on the 'cross stone' crystal, it refers to the Southern Cross constellation that guided Maori and Pakeha sailors. Aligned to the compass points, the cross casts an x-shaped shadow in the afternoon sun.

Coastal Merchant

63 Bridge Street • Nelson • 03 545 6960
info@coastalmerchant.tv • www.coastalmerchant.tv

Nelson's newest design store featuring inspirational and funky Kiwiana and Pacifica styles in home wares, clothing, gifts, art, ceramics and jewellery. A unique blend of Nelson and NZ artists and labels including in-house jewellery design by Tania Tupu.

Open: Daily 9.30am - 5.30pm in Summer, Winter, 10am - 5pm and closed Sun.

Cabbage Trees

The Cabbage Trees (ti rakau) were created by noted New Zealand corrugated iron sculptor Jeff Thomson in 2005. The cabbage tree was important to Maori - its leaves were used by guide Kehu to make sandals in the epic exploration of the Buller River with explorer Thomas Brunner.

72

Refinery Artspace

3 Halifax Street • Nelson • 03 548 1721
info@refineryartspace.org
www.refineryartspace.org

Refinery Artspace features a range of contemporary and traditional artwork in its two large exhibition spaces and sculpture garden. The retail outlet offers painting, sculpture, ceramics, jewellery, textiles and glass. Refinery Artspace supports the development of arts and cultural activities in the Nelson region by offering professional development courses and a mentoring and residency programme for emerging artists.

Open: Mon to Fri 9am – 5pm.
Sat 10am – 2pm.

Photo (left): Daniel Allen

View from the Centre of New Zealand (above). Photo: Daniel Allen

Centre of New Zealand

A short stroll from downtown Nelson, the Centre of New Zealand is a popular hill for walks. The base of the hill, The Botanics playing fields, was the scene of New Zealand's first game of rugby in 1870.

In the 1870s the chief surveyor for Nelson, John Spence Browning, undertook to connect all of the independent surveys that European settlers had carried out previously. He began the survey in Nelson and extended it south to the West Coast. Using the triangulation method of surveying, Browning took the zig zag track to the top of Botanical Hill and made this the starting point for the apex of his first set of triangles. As a result, the hill became known as the Centre of New Zealand.

Apparently the actual centre of the country is at a point in the Spooners Range in the Golden Downs Forest.

No doubt being known as The Centre of New Zealand has made the hill a far more attractive proposition for walkers and the view is well worth the effort. Fit people can make it to the top in 20 to 25 minutes.

For details about the walk and 59 others, check out the Walk Nelson and Walk Tasman series of books on sale around the region.

Wooden Chair by Chris Rendle at the Centre of New Zealand (below). Photo: Nelson City Council

Photo (above): Nelson Mail

Janet Bathgate

2 Mayroyd Terrace • Nelson
03 548 2915 • 027 430 7126
jbathgate@xtra.co.nz

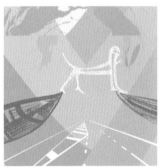

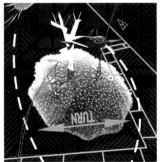

Janet is a printmaker, WearableArt™ creator and graphic designer who studied printmaking to post-graduate level at Ilam, Canterbury University. Printmaking continues to provide a creative challenge for her, especially where traditional etching and relief printing methods merge with computer-assisted techniques. Janet's work deals with the migrations of people between hemispheres, cross cultural melding and the extinctions and survivals of life on earth.

Janet's printmaking workshop is open to visitors in January only, 10am to 5pm daily. At other times please visit RED Gallery to view Janet's work.

Austin Davies
Painter

39 Cleveland Terrace • Nelson • 03 546 7221 • austindavies@clear.net.nz

Visitors welcome, but please ring first.

Jay van der Reijden

91 Brook Street • Nelson • 03 539 0697 • 021 188 0519
jayvdr@gmail.com • www.jaysartwork.com

Jay works and exhibits internationally and has been creating artworks in stone for over eleven years, exploring imagery inspired by mythology from around the world. Originally self-taught, she has gone on to study under masters the world over. Jay regularly attends symposiums and has undertaken art residencies in Ireland and China.

Open by appointment only.

77A

Warwick House

64 Brougham Street • Nelson • 03 548 3164
enquiries@warwickhouse.co.nz
www.warwickhouse.co.nz

Built in 1854, 'The Castle' is one of New Zealand's most important early Victorian Gothic style mansions. Fully restored, it offers 4+ star elegant accommodation in a quiet central city location with four luxurious suites featuring claw-foot baths. The Grand Ballroom is available for hire, tours by arrangement.

77B

Charles Shaw
Manuka Pottery

179 Collingwood Street • Nelson • shop 03 548 1452
home 03 548 2191 • chasnrose@xtra.co.nz
www.nzpotters.com/potterspages

Charles Shaw is a relentless experimenter with a workshop resembling a science lab. His recent experiments have involved crystalline glazes and the intriguing mineral effect that blooms during the firing process.

78

Fiona Sutherland
Manuka Pottery

179 Collingwood Street • Nelson • 03 548 1452
021 160 9515 • fsutherland@xtra.co.nz

Fiona is an accomplished artist who has exhibited throughout the U.K. and Australia. Born in Scotland, she studied at the Duncan of Jordanstone College of Art obtaining a B.A. (Hons) Degree in Fine Art and has since won numerous awards. She is known for her distinctive paintings and sculptures that include public artwork in cement and glass mosaic. Smaller pieces in clay are made in her workshop at Manuka Pottery.

Outlets: Rutherford Gallery and WOW® Museum, Nelson.

Bill Burke

17 Shelbourne Street
Nelson • 03 548 1120
studio@billburke.co.nz
www.billburke.co.nz

Bill's artworks capture our maritime scenery, exquisite views of New Zealand life and the essential subtleties of human and animal characteristics.

To visit Bill's studio gallery (a three minute stroll from Nelson's landmark Cathedral) please call by or phone for opening hours.

Paintings (clockwise from left) - 'Jack Guard, Boatbuilder' (oil), 'Nin's Bin, Kaikoura' (oil), 'Kawarau Gorge, Queenstown' (oil) and 'Clinker' (pastel)

80

Margot Rowling

377 Trafalgar Street • Nelson • 027 220 6550
margotrowling@yahoo.co.nz

Margot works in acrylic, oil and mixed media.
Her paintings are a visual diary of experiences
and places – not a replication, but the mood
and expression of a moment in time.
Visit by appointment only.

81

Dana Rose Studio Gallery

13 Van Diemen Street • Nelson • 03 548 3379
021 051 3894 • artist@paradise.net.nz
www.danarose.co.nz

Dana's imaginative compositions in rich, evocative colours are difficult to categorise but easy to appreciate; buyers comment that they never tire of looking at them. A professional painter and tutor for over 10 years, Dana has won several awards. Price range:$150 – $3,000.

Open most days, please ring first.

Entrance to Brian Strong's Studio (below). Photo: Daniel Allen

Brian C Strong
Dip.F.A. (Hons)

89 Mount Street • Nelson
03 548 8766 • bstrong@xtra.co.nz
www.briancstrong.co.nz

Using canvas and paper with edges torn to replicate parchment, Brian creates paintings that capture the spirit and essence of New Zealand. The use of printed images of maps and treaty documents adds a cross-cultural element to his work, while divisions in the paintings create a sense of time and contrast in space. Brian's paintings are unique and highly sought after.

Studio open: Daily 10am - 4.30pm or by appointment.

Dean Hawkins Jewellery

31 Jenner Road • Nelson • 03 548 0387 • info@deanhawkins.co.nz
www.deanhawkins.co.nz

Dean Hawkins is well known as a creator of quality original jewellery with distinctive character and individual flair. From the Kiwiana collection to more sophisticated European-inspired pieces, his contemporary yet timeless designs are unmistakable.

Dean Hawkins Jewellery is highly regarded for quality craftsmanship and original design and is available online or at Shine and The Suter Art Gallery in Nelson.

For commissions contact the artist directly. Visit by appointment.

84

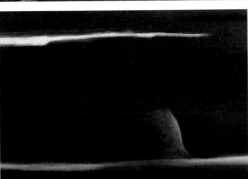

Nic Foster

B.V.A. (NMIT) B.A. (Hons) Ilam
School of Fine Art

7 Emano Street • Nelson • 03 548 1211
021 139 1715 • info@nicfoster.co.nz
www.nicfoster.com

"...sublime work of atmosphere, light,
darkness and drama." – *Nelson Mail, 2007*

"Foster's work is technically and
emotionally very fine." – *Nelson Mail, 2006*

Nic's expert use of oil painting techniques
has seen his work become sought after
both locally and internationally.

Represented by: Catchment Gallery,
Nelson; River East, Greytown; Left Bank
Gallery, Greymouth.

Price range: $500 – $5,000.
Studio visits welcomed – please call first.

Kerstiens

36 Gloucester Street • Nelson • 03 546 6980
enquiries@kerstiens.co.nz • www.kerstiens.co.nz

Kerstiens believe in creating a wonderful experience by hand crafting chocolate and fudge using ingredients from around the world, while still maintaining their own Kiwi style. The result - the finest handmade chocolates and luxury treats you could ever wish for.

85B

85C

Laroque, South of France

Linda Richards

6 Washington Terace • Nelson • 03 548 2748
021 942 718 • lindarichards@xtra.co.nz

Linda's travels and love of New Zealand are reflected in her widely appealing art.

Price range: $60 - $3,000.
Viewing by appointment, please phone first.

Cathy Jones

Flat 1 • 47a Washington Road • Nelson • 03 546 9499
027 546 9499 • cjthebot@hotmail.com

Cathy Jones is a botanist who expresses her fascination with nature and the human form in bold acrylics and watercolours.
Viewing by appointment.

Port Hills & Waterfront

Head out of town along Haven Road and just before the corner of Russell Street you will find a place that hums with the sound of conversation and a coffee grinder.

When Dan Hennah (Jr) quit working in Wellington's film industry and returned to his hometown to launch Sublime Coffee, many of the locals thought he was mad. Three years on it is well on the way to becoming a Nelson institution.

Possibly the only street in Nelson with a dairy at both ends, historic Russell Street is steep, full of character and the area is practically crawling with artists. Not only is it where you will find Jane Evans and her celebrated cottage and studio, but the

Navigator sculpture by Tim Wraight (above). Photo: Nelson City Council. View of Fifeshire Rock from Rocks Road (below). Photo: Daniel Allen

Seafarers Memorial Wharf (above). Photo: Nelson Tasman Tourism. Seagull on the Early Settlers Memorial Wall (below). Photo: Daniel Allen

area is also home to 2005 Montana World of WearableArt™ Awards Supreme Award winner and former Green MP Mike Ward, and painters Kathryn Furniss and Anna Leary.

From the teal blue of the water and the silhouette of Haulashore Island at dusk, to the ghostly sight of container ships on the horizon and the classic lighthouse, Nelson's waterfront is more than a visual feast - it's a 12-course degustation dinner with chips.

Points of interest include the Early Settlers Memorial Wall and Statue near Saltwater Café. The wall features plaques recording the names of the 235 ships and 5,500 European pioneers who arrived in Nelson between 1841 and 1850. The bronze statue by Anthony Stones gives us an idea of how those first Pakeha (European) would have looked, especially if someone had dipped them in chocolate just before they reached land.

A little further along Wakefield Quay you'll come to the Seafarers' Memorial Wharf, the scene of Nelson's annual Blessing of the Fleet. Next to the Nelson Yacht Club, the wharf's centrepiece is a dramatic bronze sculpture by Grant Palliser of a seaman at the wheel of a boat in heavy weather.

Either of these two locations provides a perfect spot for a picnic of fish and chips.

As you cruise past Haulashore Island on your way to Tahunanui Beach you can't miss Fifeshire Rock, named after the ship that brought the first European settlers to Nelson in 1842. Just before you reach Tahunanui Beach there's a fantastic spot for high tide swimming known locally as "the wall". Some steep steps and a handrail built into the wall guide you down for a plunge into Tasman Bay.

88A

88B

Sublime Coffee

211 Haven Road • Nelson • 03 539 4988
dan_hennah@yahoo.com

"Great coffee. a nice smooth, creamy texture and a rich flavour...I rate it 10/10" – Shadow, 2008.

Enjoy the Sublime Coffee experience at selected locations throughout the top of the South Island, or come direct to the source for your own bean supply.

Gael Montgomerie

28 Stanley Crescent • Nelson • 03 548 4409
gaelmontgomerie@xtra.co.nz

Gael invites commissions from clients seeking a contemporary approach to the portrait genre. Phone first to visit her garden studio above Nelson Haven.

Sublime Café (below). Photo: Daniel Allen

89

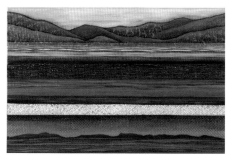

Kathryn Furniss

209 Haven Rd • Nelson • 03 546 7157 • 027 244 6991
kfurniss@xtra.co.nz
www.artfind.co.nz/artist/kathfurn

Kathryn creates heavily textured acrylic and mixed media paintings inspired by the Pacific lifestyle, landscapes and objects. Recently she has been exploring other mediums and

collaborating with her husband to produce a range of garden sculpture and wall hangings in aluminium.

Kathryn's home and studio is an historic house 15 minutes walk from the city centre. Studio/Gallery open by appointment.

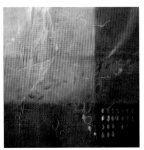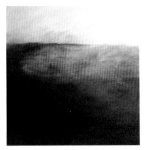

Anna Leary

BVA • Toss Woollaston Scholarship

50 Queens Road • Nelson • 03 546 6882 • 021 542 438
info@AnnaLeary.com • www.AnnaLeary.com

"Leary is an archivist of time, recording in colour the complex interplay of light on land and sea..." *Anna-Marie White, The Suter Art Gallery.*

Set against a backdrop of Nelson's bustling port and Tasman Bay, Anna's home showcases the work and inspirations of a diverse artist. Her series reference her Pacific location, iconic sites and human nature.
Anna regularly creates artworks on a commission basis, developing bespoke interpretive works documenting the stories of people and place.

"It will make the artwork extra special now that we've met you and taken part in creating it."
Kathryn & Neil, Sydney

View at the WOW® Museum, Nelson; www.AnnaLeary.com, or phone to make an appointment.
Price range $500-$5,000.

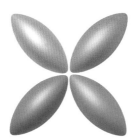

Boats on Nelson Harbour (above). Photo: Nelson Tasman Tourism

92

Photo (below): Marion van Dijk

Sightseeing

Irvine Major(1922-2000) Summer in Nelson 1960, oil on canvas 810 x 1050mm. Purchased in 2001. *The Suter Art Gallery Collection*.

Early Settlers Statue

The bronze Early Settlers Statue shows a family arriving on Wakefield Quay in 1842. It was commissioned in 2005 and created by former Nelson sculptor Anthony Stones.

Aotearoa Mural

Aotearoa was painted by mural artist Chris Finlayson in 1984. Scenery, window structure and clouds are set into a painted carved timber panel.

Seafarers Memorial

The Seafarers Memorial, commissioned by the Seafarers Memorial Trust and created by Grant Palliser in 2001, stands as a memorial to fishers lost at sea. The bronze seaman at his wheel is the centrepiece of the ship's bridge-shaped Sunderland Marine Pier.

Johanna Tyson

23 Fifeshire Crescent • Nelson • 03 548 1944
021 060 7484 • tysonfamily@actrix.co.nz

Johanna works from her home overlooking the sea, painting the light and environment that she loves.

Appointments welcome.

94

Craig Potton

46 Britannia Heights • Nelson
03 548 9009
pottonc@xtra.co.nz
www.craigpotton.co.nz

Craig Potton is one of New Zealand's leading landscape photographers. He has photographed extensively in New Zealand, its sub-Antarctic islands and the Dry Valleys of Antarctica. He has also worked as a location/stills photographer on the Lord of the Rings, Peter Pan and The Lion, The Witch and The Wardrobe movies.

Craig is the founder of Craig Potton Publishing, based here in Nelson. His photographic books are available from good bookshops and his photographic work is available online, at Catchment Gallery or by appointment (phone Kim or Emma on 03 548 9009)

95A

Photos: (left) Daniel Allen and (above) Elspeth Collier

Wakefield Quay House Luxury Accommodation

Woodi & John Moore

385 Wakefield Quay • Nelson • 03 546 7275
027 265 7547 • wakefieldquay@xtra.co.nz
www.wakefieldquay.co.nz

Relax and watch the yachts in the harbour entrance from the sunny decks of this restored 1905 villa with panoramic sea to mountain views. Enjoy a warm welcome from artistic and nautically minded hosts, complimentary evening drinks and delicious gourmet breakfasts. Come sailing with Sail Nelson.

95B

Photo (below): Marion van Dijk

Sightseeing

Jane Evans ONZM (1946 -) Saturday Afternoon 1976 (detail), oil and acrylic on board 610 x 740mm. Presented by the estate of Amelia F. Roe in 2004. *The Suter Art Gallery Collection*.

96A

96B

Ralph Hetzel
Port Pots

41 Whitby Road • Nelson • 03 546 8391 • 027 449 3380
pelican@ts.co.nz

Handcrafted ceramic seagulls each with their own unique personality.

Nelson Outlets: South Street Gallery, Pots 'n' Prints, WOW® Museum, Magnificent New Zealand, The Cool Store Gallery.

Open: Daily 9am - 5pm.

96C

Mary Andrews
Spiral Studio

42 Chamboard Place • Nelson • 03 546 6204
maryandrews@ihug.co.nz • www.fibrespectrum.co.nz
www.creativetourism.co.nz

Fibre artist Mary Andrews works from 'Spiral Studio' nestled within the beautiful Nelson hills. Mary utilises the natural properties of fleece to transform raw fibre into functional art forms, felting and weaving wall hangings, hats, bags and cushions. She runs regular felt making workshops using colourful hand-dyed fleece.

Price range: $30 - $3,000+

Please make an appointment for Spiral Studio. Work can be purchased at Fibre Spectrum (page 64D), Trafalgar Street, Nelson.

Lou-Darcie

5 Whitby Road • Nelson • 03 539 0606 • 021 110 1501
faerilou@actrix.co.nz

Lou-Darcie explores the themes of beauty, mortality, virtue and loss with a highly narrative, illustrative style that laces the innocent with the macabre.

Photo (below): Marion van Dijk

Sightseeing

Charles Blomfield (1848-1926) Fifeshire Rock
1871 (detail), oil on board 378 x 477mm.
Bequeathed by Mrs B.H. Sharp of New Plymouth
in 1981. *The Suter Art Gallery Collection.*

Tahunanui Beach and Fifeshire Rock (below). Photo: Daniel Allen

Tahunanui

N

GOLF CL

NELSON AIRPORT

108B

110A

POINT RD

HOULT CRES

ALLPORT PL

SEAVIEW RD

NORWICH

109A

108C

DURHAM ST

KENT ST

DERBY ST

MONACO

BALMORAL PL

DEVON ST

109B

108A

STEAD CRES

SONGER ST

LUSTY PL

ASHBURY ST

TENNYSON CRES

WHAKATU DRIVE

ALDINGA AVE

TYREE DR

DICKENS ST

MONACO VIEW

RAILWAY RESERVE

6

KENDALL VIEW

MARLOWE ST

BYRON PL

MAIN RD

111

POLST NIK

▼ SEE PAGE 113

TAHUNANUI BEACH

TAHUNANUI

NELSON SOUTH

TOKE

Tahunanui

A visit to Nelson without a walk on Tahunanui Beach is a bit like going to New York and never making it to Central Park.

Tahuna, as the locals call it, is one of the places that defines Nelson. It's safe for swimming, long enough to really stretch your legs and reputed to be one of world's best spots for kite surfing. Its back beach is also a hit with dogs. A virtual Mecca for canines, the back beach is a great place to see dogs of all shapes and sizes chasing sticks, barking at seagulls and going for a swim.

If you're feeling peckish there is plenty of food on offer at the local shops. Pots 'n' Prints is well worth a look, especially if you're after a unique souvenir or a gift.

Just down the road you'll come to Annesbrook, home of WOW®'s global head quarters - the World of WearableArt™ and Classic Car Museum. From the museum, founder Suzie Moncrieff and her team gather the entries from around the world, judge the garments and plan each year's show.

A visit to the museum is the closest thing you can get to experiencing an actual WOW® show. There is a feast of award-winning and memorable creations from WOW®'s history on display and, best of all, you get to see them up close. The car museum is where you'll discover over 50 gleaming vehicles from late 19th century inventions through to modern classics all in mint condition.

The complex also boasts Reflections Art Gallery specialising in New Zealand contemporary art. The gallery exhibits mainly paintings and sculptures by established and emerging artists.

Over the years the gallery has exhibited work by big name artists like Philip Trusttum but you're just as likely to see work by recent art school graduates.

Runner at sunset along Tahunanui Beach (left). Photo: Daniel Allen

The Abel Tasman Statue

Abel Tasman Statue, in the car park at Tahunanui Beach, was sculpted by Anthony Stones in the UK and erected in 2000. It is a life size bronze depiction of the 17th century Dutch explorer, Abel Janszoon Tasman and was gifted to the region by Dutch immigrants.

Change of Tack Sculpture

Change of Tack in the carpark at Tahunanui Beach was sculpted by Michael MacMillan 2008. The sailing inspired sculpture is made up of two sails in stainless steel, concrete and resin, and together they weigh approximately three tonnes.

Tahunanui Beach (below). Photo: Nelson Tasman Tourism

102

Nikki Huizinga

8 Istana Place • Nelson • 03 546 4684
huizinga@woosh.co.nz

Supreme Winner – 2008 Nelson Regional Art Awards

Nikki is an established artist who specialises in large contemporary landscapes. Her oil paintings achieve a unique depth, through use of layering techniques and careful attention to colour complexity and balance.

Nelson outlets: RED Gallery and Rutherford Gallery. Studio visits by appointment only.

Pots 'n' Prints

Ainslie Riddoch

16A Tahunanui Drive • Tahunanui • Nelson
03 546 4992 • ainslieriddoch@yahoo.co.nz

Pots 'n' Prints is a vibrant, colour-filled gallery and craft shop in an old villa near Tahunanui Beach, offering a wide selection of work from the artists and craftspeople of Nelson and New Zealand. The beautiful pieces on display include pottery, paintings, limited edition prints, jewellery, sculpture, textiles, art cards and more.

Mail order and pack and post available (New Zealand and overseas).

Open: Daily in Summer, closed Sundays in Winter.

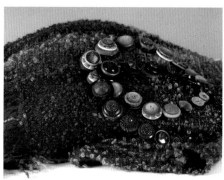

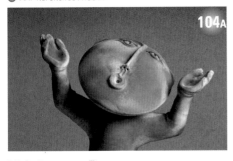

Waimea Pottery

Paul Laird

7 Grenville Terrace • Tahunanui • Nelson • 03 548 5162
021 146 6272 • paul.laird@xtra.co.nz
www.ceramicartist.co.nz

Paul Laird creates decorative and functional clay objects for the home and garden. Accommodation in a stylish new apartment with expansive sea views is also offered.

Price range: $25-$2,000. Outlets: Up the Garden Path, Motueka; Riverside Gallery, Nelson. Open: 9am-5pm, please phone first.

Katy Sanson Oils & Watercolours

9 Stansell Avenue • Tahunanui • Nelson • 03 546 4054
021 027 92311 • katysanson@xtra.co.nz
www.katysanson.co.nz

Katy explores the full possibilities of paint and brush to produce technically challenging works that capture the essence of the subject.

View by appointment.

Tahunanui Beach (below). Photo: Daniel Allen

Nelson Glasshouse

Frances Woodhead

41 Tosswill Road • Tahunanui • Nelson • 03 546 5265
021 239 5659 • info@nelsonglasshouse.co.nz
www.nelsonglasshouse.co.nz

Frances creates original and affordable pieces from 100% recycled kiln-formed glass. She also runs workshops for beginners. Her work is available at The Suter Art Gallery or at her studio, by appointment.

Larisse Hall

27 Stafford Avenue • Annesbrook
Nelson • 03 547 4929
027 358 2006
larisse@larissehall.co.nz
www.larissehall.co.nz

Simple pencil sketches or bold and passionate works on canvas, Larisse incorporates relief with multiple layers of water-based media.

Constantly evolving, Larisse exhibits regularly and invites you to her courtyard studio, on Fridays 10am - 2pm (other times by appointment).

Commissions welcome. Price range: $35 - $3,000.

World of WearableArt™ and Classic Cars Museum

Cadillac Way (off Quarantine Road) • Nelson
03 547 4573 • info@wowcars.co.nz
www.wowcars.co.nz

Firmly established as an iconic Nelson attraction, the WOW® Museum celebrates two distinctly different passions, providing a creative visual feast.

Be blown away by the incredible garments that feature in the WearableArt™ Gallery and marvel at the extraordinary imagination of the artists who have created them.

Then visit the world-class collection of 50 classic and rare cars, beautifully displayed under theatrical lighting in the Classic Cars Museum.

Open: Daily 10am - 5pm, except Christmas Day.

Artwork: 28 Days, Tasman Bay by Anna Leary

Reflections Art Gallery

WOW® Museum

- -

Cadillac Way (off Quarantine Road) • Nelson
03 547 4573 • reflections@wowcars.co.nz
www.wowcars.co.nz

- -

Reflections Art Gallery is located in the heart of the World of WearableArt™ and Classic Cars Museum, offering exciting contemporary New Zealand paintings, sculptures, prints, photographs, jewellery, glass and ceramic works from both emerging and established artists. Exhibitions change on a regular basis.

Entry is free.

Open: Daily 10am – 5pm, except Christmas Day.

Broadgreen House

276 Nayland Road • Stoke • 03 547 0403
Broadgreen@ncc.govt.nz

Broadgreen Historic House is a fine example of a mid 1850's Cobb house, meticulously furnished to replicate a family home of the period. Guided tours available. A small entry charge applies.

Open: Daily 10.30am - 4.30pm, visitors welcome.

Art at the Airport

Renovations to the original airport building incorporated local art, including Pacific Angel, sculpted from Oamaru stone by Nelson artist Bodhi Vincent in 1995. This sculpture is based on the angel motif that was the then WearableArt™ symbol.

The Airport also has artwork by Darryl Frost and other local artists.

Grand Mercure Nelson Monaco

6 Point Road • Monaco • Nelson • 03 547 8233
hotel@monacoresort.co.nz • www.monacoresort.co.nz

Located just minutes from the heart of Nelson, Grand Mercure Nelson Monaco is the perfect retreat. The resort provides all the comforts and conveniences you could wish for including award winning restaurant The Orangerie, health and beauty spa, pool, gym, boutique jeweller, hairdressing salon and conference facilities.

109A

109B

Tidal Access Gallery

Brian Flintoff

89 Point Road • Monaco • Nelson • 03 547 3350
027 447 3340 • brian@jadeandbone.co.nz
www.jadeandbone.co.nz

Traditional Maori art inspires Brian's bone carvings, prints and musical instruments, which are complemented by his book 'Taonga Puoro, Singing Treasures'.

Brian's gallery by the estuary is open most days but phoning first is advised.

The Point Studio

Nikki Johnson

107 Point Road • Monaco • Nelson • 03 547 6550
021 105 5777 • the.point@orcon.net.nz

The Point Studio established in 1988 offers unique paua, glass and silver art. A café is now open on site with the best view by the sea.

Open: Daily from 10am.

Photo (below): Marion van Dijk

Sightseeing

F.V. Hall (1897-1987) The Inlet, Monaco (n.d.),
oil on canvas 870 x 720mm. Presented by Miss
Brenda de Butts in 1973. *The Suter Art Gallery
Collection.*

View of Monaco & beyond (below). Photo: Nelson Tasman Tourism

Fumio Noguchi

604 Main Road • Stoke • Nelson • 03 547 0229
fumio.noguchi@xtra.co.nz

Fumio started carving in Christchurch under the guidance of Maori carver David Paki. He predominantly creates practical pieces from deer antlers, bone and hardwood including pendants inspired by Maori designs. Fumio, a descendant of a Japanese Samurai, also enjoys carving Japanese 'Netsuke'. See Fumio at Nelson Saturday Market or make an appointment to visit.

Commissions are welcome.

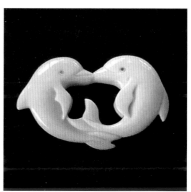

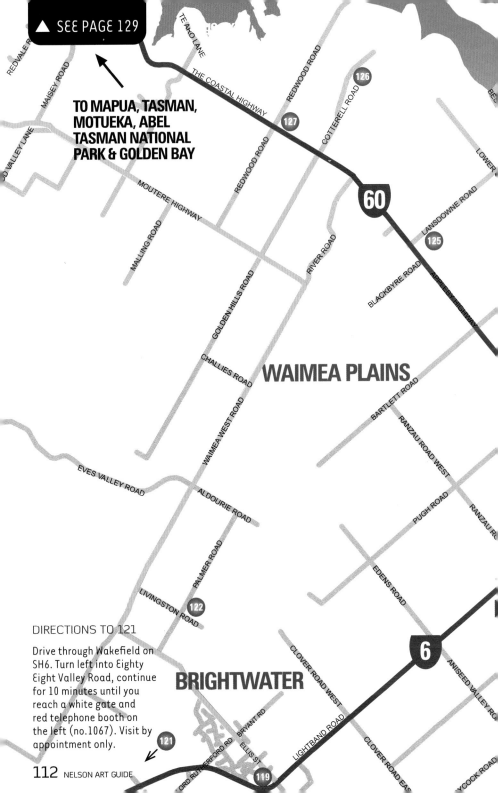

▲ SEE PAGE 129

TO MAPUA, TASMAN, MOTUEKA, ABEL TASMAN NATIONAL PARK & GOLDEN BAY

THE COASTAL HIGHWAY

TE AHO LANE

REDVALE R

MAISEY ROAD

D VALLEY LANE

MOUTERE HIGHWAY

MALLING ROAD

REDWOOD ROAD

REDWOOD ROAD

COTTERELL ROAD

126

127

BES

LOWER

60

LANSDOWNE ROAD

125

BLACKBYRE ROAD

ABBEY BY HIGHWAY

RIVER ROAD

GOLDEN HILLS ROAD

CHALLIES ROAD

WAIMEA PLAINS

BARTLETT ROAD

RANZAU ROAD WEST

WAIMEA WEST ROAD

EVES VALLEY ROAD

ALDOURIE ROAD

PUGH ROAD

RANZAU R

PALMER ROAD

LIVINGSTON ROAD

122

EDENS ROAD

6

DIRECTIONS TO 121

Drive through Wakefield on SH6. Turn left into Eighty Eight Valley Road, continue for 10 minutes until you reach a white gate and red telephone booth on the left (no.1067). Visit by appointment only.

BRIGHTWATER

CLOVER ROAD WEST

ANISEED VALLEY RO

BRYANT RD

ELLIS ST

LIGHTBAND ROAD

CLOVER ROAD EAS

YCOCK ROAD

121

ORD RUTHERFORD RD

119

Waimea

TO NELSON

N

6

STOKE

SANDEMAN ROAD

HEADINGLY LANE

116

117

CSHANE ROAD

LOWER QUEEN STREET

118

QUEEN STREET

RICHMOND

BATEUP ROAD

115B

HART ROAD

HILL STREET

TE ROAD

KINGS RISE

115A

HILL STREET SOUTH

Waimea Estuary looking towards the Richmond Ranges. Photo: Daniel Allen

Waimea Plains & Beyond

Famous for its orchards and vineyards, the Waimea Plains stretch south of Nelson and include Richmond, Hope, Brightwater and Wakefield.

Peaceful, friendly and still distinctively rural, a day spent in the area might include visiting artists in their studios, going for a horse trek, visiting a winery, learning how to throw a pot and having a swim in a beautiful river.

Waimea is an unassuming place. It produced Lord Ernest Rutherford and the first ever World of WearableArt™ Awards, yet the area doesn't exactly hog the limelight. Possibly because people are just too busy getting on with it.

One artist who has made his mark on the plains is potter Royce McGlashen who, after 30 years in Brightwater, still describes the place as "wonderful". He says the hills and mountains that surround the plains are constant sources of inspiration and distraction.

"You can come out of your workshop and see snow, forestry, farming - there is always something happening," he says.

Further south in 88 Valley lives American-born artist Princess Hart. An artist with few creative boundaries, Princess is best known for her amazingly lifelike paintings and etchings, many of which portray rural scenes. She says much of her inspiration comes from the Waimea area. "Farming communities pace themselves with the seasons and I like that," she says.

To make the most of what Waimea has to offer make sure you get off the highway and go exploring. Drives up the Aniseed and Lee Valleys are must-dos not only for the landscape and views, but in the warmer months they are great for swimming.

A drive to the stunning Lake Rotoiti, St Arnaud and Nelson Lakes National Park is also a great way to spend a day. It's about 100km from Richmond to St Arnaud so give yourself a bit over an hour to get there.

115A

115B

Margaret Johnston

5 Kings Rise • Richmond • 03 544 5650 • 027 274 7880
relax@sunnybank.co.nz

Margaret produces sculptures ranging from large stone works to small bronzes and bold, expressive paintings. She displays her work in her Mediterranean styled home and one and a half acre panoramic garden in the Richmond foothills.

Please phone to arrange a visit. Price range: $400 – $5,000. Commissions welcomed.

Alchemy Arts

92 Bateup Road • Richmond • 03 544 5853
hsmacmillan@xtra.co.nz • www.alchemyarts.co.nz

Alchemy Arts - encompassing MacMillans Ceramics gallery, interactive decorating and clay work opportunities, John Fry Woodwork and 'The Boutique' Nelson designer clothing. Alchemy Cafe on site, fully licensed with all-weather courtyard and family friendly environs.

Open: Daily 10am – 4pm, except public holidays.

116

Safari Furniture

Lance Tighe

50 Headingly Lane • Richmond • 021 167 2658
safarifurniture@slingshot.co.nz
www.safarifurniture.co.nz

Lance creates hand-sculpted pieces from various timbers and metals with a passion for detail and commitment to style. With many one-off pieces, Safari Furniture is as individual as the buyer.

Sundial Square in Richmond (below). Photo: Caroline Moreton

Eyebright

McShane Road • Richmond
03 544 4977
office@eyebright.co.nz
www.eyebright.co.nz

Eyebright is a well known tourist icon and one of New Zealand's most loved stores. In the midst of café and wine country in beautiful gardens it is just minutes drive from Richmond town centre. Eyebright specialises in magnificent artful floral displays using silk decor flowers and an extensive jewellery range sourced from New Zealand and around the world. These include pieces in the Indulgence and Highlightz ranges, designed and made on site by co-owner Adrienne Owen.

Open: Daily 9.30am - 5pm excluding Christmas Day, Boxing Day, Good Friday and Anzac Day.

118

Waimea Estates

Café in the Vineyard at Waimea Estates

Appleby Highway • Hope • Nelson • 03 544 4963
cafe@waimeaestates.co.nz • www.waimeaestates.co.nz

"Waimea Estates is emerging as a stand-out success." — *leading NZ wine writer Michael Cooper*

Café in the Vineyard is open for indoor/outdoor lunchtime dining among the vines, cellar door tastings and sales of Waimea and Spinyback wines. Live music is performed on Sundays and exhibitions of local art run continuously.
Tours and tastings available by arrangement.

Open: Summer, daily 11am - 5pm.
For winter hours, please phone before visiting.

McGlashen Pottery

Royce McGlashen

128 Ellis Street • Brightwater • Nelson
03 542 3585 • pottery@ts.co.nz
www.roycemcglashen.co.nz

Visit Royce's studio to view his wide range of functional tableware designed to reflect New Zealand culture and enhance current culinary trends. He also creates ceramic art, contemporary paintings and pieces for the garden, and has collected many awards in his 40+ years exploring his passion for clay.

Royce's gallery is situated beside the main highway in Brightwater, 21 kms south of Nelson.

Open: Mon to Fri 10am – 5pm.
Weekends 10am – 5pm from mid Dec to Easter and 10am – 4pm after Easter to mid Dec.

Stoneyhill Studio & Press

Princess Hart

1067 – 88 Valley Road • RD1 Wakefield • 03 541 9558
fax 03 541 8887 • stoneyhill@clear.net.nz
www.w3art.com/PrincessHart

Princess Hart is a multi-disciplined artist whose creativity embraces painting, printmaking, drawing and sculpture. Well known for her large-scale paintings, she also creates full-colour etchings from multiple copper plates using traditional printmaking techniques. Princess's design skills also extend into architectural art – she created the base-relief on the Mount Campbell Communications building in Tahunanui.

Classically trained as an illustrator, she was one of only 26 women globally to win entry into the prestigious Communication Arts 41st Illustration Annual. Princess's artworks appear in more than 140 international museum, corporate and private collections, including the National Gallery in Washington D.C.

Please contact Stoneyhill Studio & Press for gallery information. Visit by appointment only.

Photo (top): Printmaking studio

Abraham's legacy… the eve of Idul Adha: mixed media, acrylic with multiple glazes on canvas, 1200 x 920mm

Sacred Heart…first fish of Tu: mixed media, acrylic with multiple glazes on canvas, 600 x 600mm

Faithkeeper… hold fast to the faith, hold fast to love, hold fast to the law: mixed media, acrylic with multiple glazes on canvas, 500 x 200mm

Opposite page: Ascention through Jordan's Gate… a journey with my soul… : mixed media, acrylic, multiple glazes and applied gold leaf on canvas, 1820 x 920mm

Toward Mapua

Whenever I'm on the road from Nelson to Motueka, I feel sorry for people who don't drive. Long straights, sweeping bends, beautiful vistas, mountain ranges and the sea - no matter what I'm driving, I always feel like I'm in an advertisement for the latest Audi.

Heading out of Richmond, the best route to take is down Lower Queen Street. Straight as an arrow, the road will take you past one of the region's mightiest industrial accomplishments - Nelson Pine Industries. It may not be pretty but the factory provides 265 full time jobs and, as managing director Murray Sturgeon is always quick to point out, the only thing coming out of its chimneys is "saturated air". My mate Guy and his kids call it "the cloud factory."

Lower Queen Street turns left into Lansdowne Road where you'll find the world class Höglund Art Glass Studio and Gallery.

Nelson Pine Industries Plant (below)

Kaimira Wines

97 Livingston Road • Brightwater • 03 542 3491
sales@kaimirawines.com • www.kaimirawines.com

Kaimira is a family-owned winery producing a wide range of high-quality, carboNZero^{Cert™} certified wines under the brands Kaimira Estate and Brightside. The tasting room is also a small gallery, showing works by local artists.

Open: 11am - 5pm from late October (Labour weekend) until 1 April.

Redwood Valley. Photo: Seifried Vineyards

Höglund Art Glass Studio & Gallery

Ola Höglund & Marie Simberg-Höglund

Lansdowne Road • Appleby • Richmond
03 544 6500 • artglass@hoglund.co.nz
www.hoglundartglass.com

World-renowned glass artists Ola Höglund and Marie Simberg-Höglund welcome you to experience the ancient art of glassmaking. Art glass by Ola and Marie is totally unique, exploring the fluid brilliance of crystal glass and the beauty of the natural environment. Ola and Marie are internationally recognised artists with work in public and private collections worldwide. Each one-of-a-kind masterpiece is a singular work of art engraved and signed by the artist - an investment and true collector's treasure.

Open: Daily 10am – 5pm all year. Closed Good Friday, Christmas and Boxing Day.

Sally Burton

72 Cotterells Road • RD1 • Appleby • 03 544 2863 • 027 277 6676
s.j.burton@xtra.co.nz • www.sallyburton.co.nz

Sally Burton's studio is in a rural setting on the edge of the Waimea Plains. Her work is inspired by the big skies over Tasman Bay and the shifting light where land meets the sea.

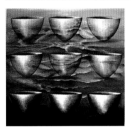

"The paintings push far beyond their undeniable decorative quality into the realm of mythical symbol." T.J. McNamara, N.Z. Herald

Sally welcomes visits by appointment at her studio in Appleby. For more details see www.sallyburton.co.nz

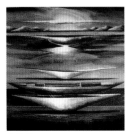

Artwork (top to bottom): River Thieves ... acrylic on tapa cloth on canvas. 80x80cm.
Milk Bowls ... acrylic on canvas. 70x70cm. Voyagers ... acrylic on canvas. 70x70cm

Seifried Estate

Corner State Highway 60 & Redwood Road
Appleby • Nelson • 03 544 1555
wines@seifried.co.nz • www.seifried.co.nz

From the beautiful Waimea Plains come the inspired and innovative wines of the South Island's oldest family winery, Seifried Estate. Enjoy fabulous local cuisine and stunning wine in a delightful vineyard setting. Facilities include a children's playground.

Cellar door open daily for wine tasting and sales.

Waimea Inlet looking towards Richmond Ranges (below). Photo: Daniel Allen

▲ SEE PAGE 155

Coastal Highway & Moutere

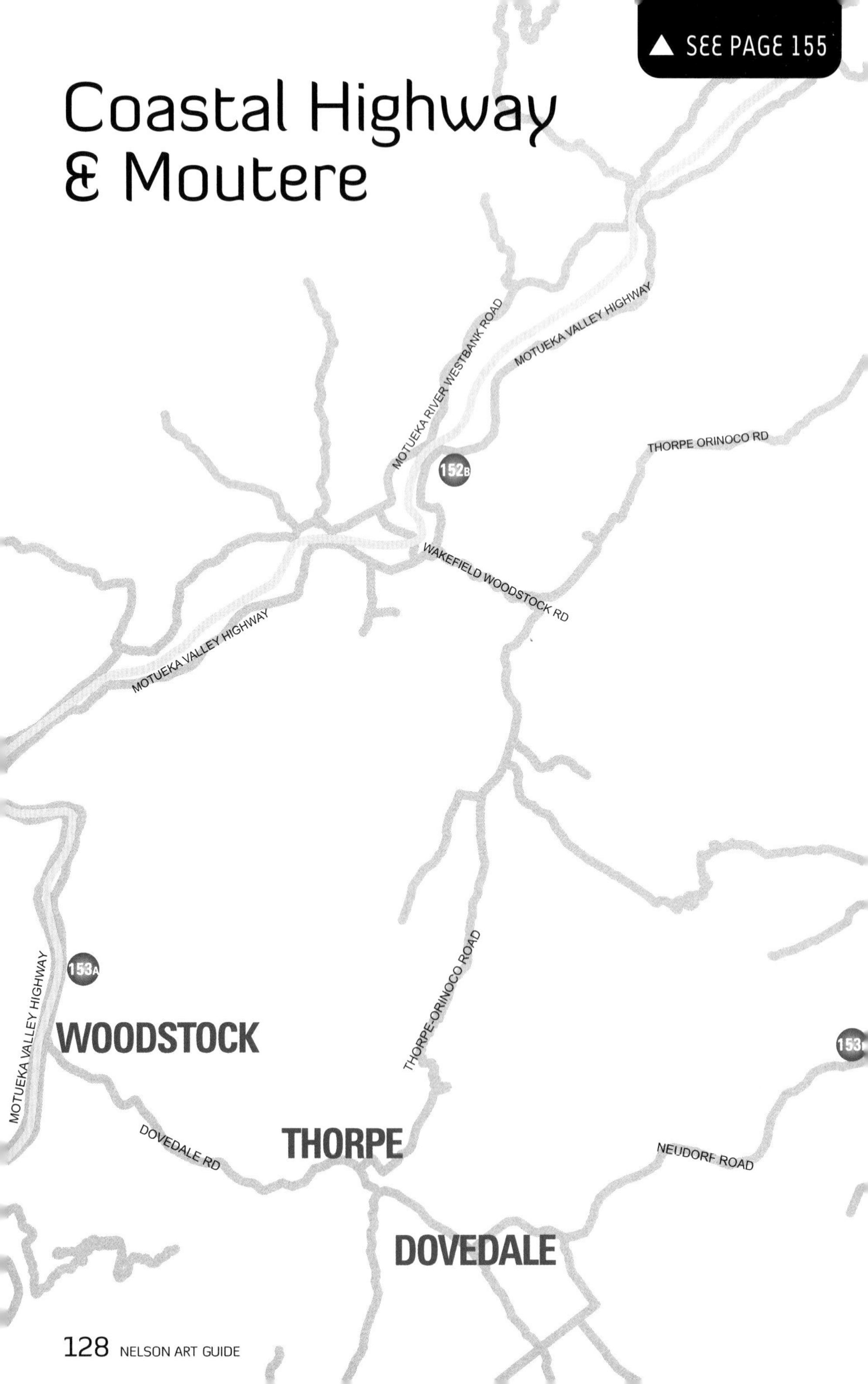
MOTUEKA RIVER WESTBANK ROAD
MOTUEKA VALLEY HIGHWAY
THORPE ORINOCO RD
152B
WAKEFIELD WOODSTOCK RD
MOTUEKA VALLEY HIGHWAY
153A
MOTUEKA VALLEY HIGHWAY
WOODSTOCK
THORPE-ORINOCO ROAD
153
DOVEDALE RD
THORPE
NEUDORF ROAD
DOVEDALE

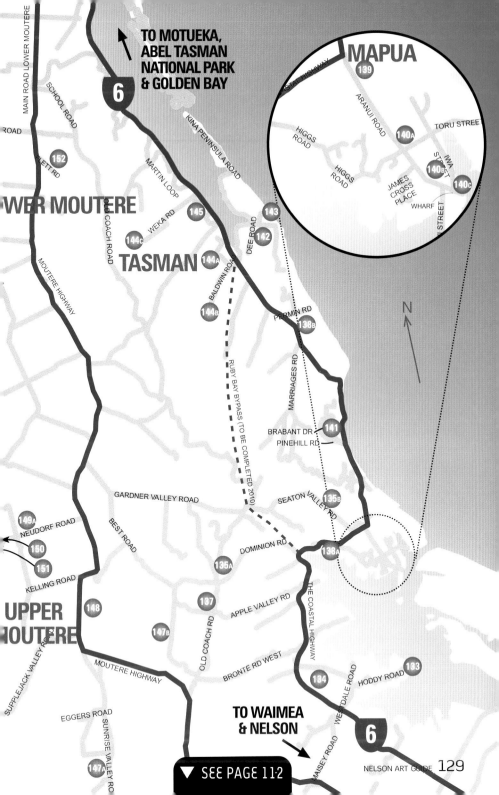

TO MOTUEKA, ABEL TASMAN NATIONAL PARK & GOLDEN BAY

6

MAPUA

139

ASTAT HIGHWAY

ARANUI ROAD

HIGGS ROAD

140A

TORU STREE

HIGGS ROAD

IWA STREET

140B

JAMES CROSS PLACE

140C

WHARF

STREET

MAIN ROAD LOWER MOUTERE

SCHOOL ROAD

ROAD

152

HETT RD

WER MOUTERE

MARTIN LOOP

KINA PENINSULA ROAD

WEKA RD

145

COACH ROAD

144C

TASMAN

144A

DEE ROAD

143

142

BALDWIN ROAD

144B

MOUTERE HIGHWAY

PERMIN RD

138B

MARRIAGES RD

N

RUBY BAY BYPASS (TO BE COMPLETED 2010)

BRABANT DR

141

PINEHILL RD

GARDNER VALLEY ROAD

SEATON VALLEY RD

135B

149A

NEUDORF ROAD

150

BEST ROAD

DOMINION RD

138A

151

KELLING ROAD

135A

UPPER

HOUTERE

148

137

APPLE VALLEY RD

THE COASTAL HIGHWAY

147B

OLD COACH RD

SUPPLEJACK VALLEY RD

MOUTERE HIGHWAY

BRONTE RD WEST

WESTDALE ROAD

HODDY ROAD

133

134

EGGERS ROAD

SUNRISE VALLEY RD

TO WAIMEA & NELSON

MAISEY ROAD

6

147A

▼ SEE PAGE 112

Mapua Inlet. Photo: Daniel Allen

Coastal Highway

Those who take the turn off to Mapua on the Coastal Highway will reap the rewards.

A 30 minute cruise from Nelson, the area once famous for nudists and smoked fish is one of the region's most popular destinations. Mapua Leisure Park's naturists are virtually gone, but the village now boasts a popular bakery called The Naked Bun!

These days Mapua's famous Smokehouse Café has been joined on the wharf by an aquarium and the very cool Cool Store Gallery (it's built in an old apple cool store). The wharf has to be one of New Zealand's best spots for eating fish and

chips and watching the tide come and go. Speaking of the tide, the way the water charges in and out of the inlet is an impressive reminder that the natural powers that formed the area are still at work.

Mapua made a massive impression on one of the artists who put Nelson creativity on the map - Toss Woollaston was mad about the place.

It has also made a big impression on a white heron (kotuku) known to the locals as Hamish. The closest thing Mapua has to a celebrity, Hamish returns to the waterfront from Okarito down on the West Coast each year to hang out here over winter. He has been doing this since the mid 1990s and is so famous the nearby ice cream parlour is named after him.

Mapua's residents are an artistic bunch. From contemporary furniture and pottery to portraits of corgis and ceramic chainsaws, they're full of surprises.

If ever there was a great example of a café putting a place on the map, it's the Jester House Café a few kilometres down the road in Tasman. With its medieval tartan meets environmentally-friendly Aotearoa flavour, it is also one of those few destinations that can deservedly be described as unique. Its list of distinguishing features is too long to note here but it includes: a stream full of enormous eels, a house in a shoe, a giant chess board and toaster, locally brewed beers, and arguably the world's greatest hash browns.

From Tasman it's a short drive to Kina Peninsula where you'll find sculptor-potter Darryl Frost's Playing With Fire Sculpture Garden. One of the region's most driven artists, Darryl is the only guy I know with a ceramic letterbox. Darryl's massive anagama kiln is a sight to behold, particularly when it's being fired, a spectacular event that happens twice a year. Anagama is Japanese for cave kiln and Darryl's takes five days to load, five days to fire and a week to cool down.

Just before you get to Motueka on State Highway 60 you pass through a gorgeous spot known as Mariri. Scenery-wise it's one of the loveliest parts of the region, especially when the tide is in and there is water on both sides of the road.

Mariri is also where you will discover Tim Wraight's Sealevel Studio Sculpture Gallery. Tim spent six years training with traditional Maori woodcarver John Mutu in the 1990's and one of the remarkable things about his art is the way he merges classical Maori and Pacific styles with contemporary looks. His carvings look simultaneously traditional and fresh.

Whenever I visit Tim's red shed I think, "If I were an artist, I'd want a place like this".

Stones on esturay (below) and view from the Coastal Highway (bottom)
Photos: Nelson Tasman Tourism

Kina Peninsula. Photo: Kina Beach Vineyard

Christine Boswijk Workshop

Christine Boswijk • Sculpture

Kirsten Boswijk • Tableware

190 Hoddy Road • Richmond
(turn off Coastal Highway into Westdale Road)
03 544 2600 • bosmais@xtra.co.nz
www.christineboswijkworkshop.co.nz

"Space has an atmosphere and what you put into that space will colour your awareness... the environment becomes its frame." *Louise Nevelson*

To visit the workshop please make an appointment.

Photos: (top) Mat Lowden & (middle left) Elspeth Collier

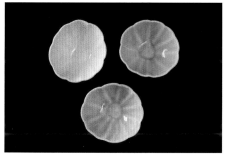

134

Grant Palliser

Westdale Road • RD1 Richmond • 03 544 6736
palliser@callsouth.net.nz • www.grantpalliser.co.nz

Grant specialises in bronze and stainless steel, creating sculptures that range from small table pieces to large site-specific commissions. He exhibits widely throughout New Zealand. The Nelson City Council's 'Sculpture Walk' publication introduces you to many of his major public works.

Grant and his partner Esmé cast the smaller bronzes and run workshops from their studio and workshop/foundry overlooking the Waimea Inlet.

Commissions welcomed, visits by appointment.

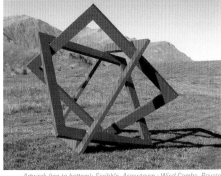

Artwork (top to bottom): Scribble, Arrowtown ; Wind Combs, Private Collection, Tasman ; Oracle II, Nelson and Lean On Me, Queenstown

David Kemp Studio

190 Dominion Road • RD1 • Upper Moutere (Turn into Dominion Rd off the Coastal Highway, the studio is signposted 2 km up the road on the right)
03 540 3720 • 021 183 1668 • dk@davidkemp.co.nz
www.davidkemp.co.nz

David's contemporary, bold, 'blokey expressionist' landscape paintings draw on his 30 years experience as a painter and sculptor and his maternal heritage in the Nelson area that dates back to 1842. View his website, chance a visit or make an appointment.

Darryl Frost's ceramic letterbox (below)

Lynn Price

Fused Glass Artist

166B Seaton Valley Rd • Mapua • 03 540 2178
021 236 4622 • lynn.price@yahoo.co.nz
www.lynnprice.co.nz

Lynn creates contemporary fused art glass, wall-pieces, gifts and stunning jewellery from her studio/gallery. Please call prior to visiting.

Photo (above): Elspeth Collier

Woollaston Estates

School Road (off Old Coach Road) • Mahana
03 543 2817 • fax 03 543 2317
www.woollaston.co.nz • mail@woollaston.co.nz

Art and fine wine form a perfect partnership at Woollaston Estates winery. Visitors are welcome to bring a picnic lunch to enjoy in the courtyard or on the lawn whilst taking in stunning views, enjoying the art and sampling wines produced in the gravity-fed winery that has been built into the hillside.

The winery also hosts a variety of events and concerts including opera and jazz performances.

The Cellar Door is open for wine tasting and sales daily 11am - 4.30pm from mid October to Easter, with live music on the lawn the first Sunday of each month.

Photo (above): Elspeth Collier

The Gallery at Woollaston

School Road (off Old Coach Road)
Mahana • 03 543 2817 • 021 393 970
www.rh-art.co.nz • thegallery@rh-art.co.nz

Adjoining the Cellar Door, The Gallery at Woollaston showcases art that is contemporary, evocative and stimulating. With a programme of public exhibitions, the gallery also sells and promotes high quality artwork by established and emerging New Zealand and international artists.

Featured artists include Laurence Aberhart, Elizabeth Thomson, Chris Charteris, Neil Dawson, Yuk King Tan, Katherine Madill, Christine Boswijk and Toss Woollaston.

The collection of permanent sculpture at Woollaston Estates includes works by Marté Szirmay, Christine Boswijk, Neil Dawson, Bill Culbert and Andrew Drummond.

Open: All year, Mon to Fri 8.30am – 5pm and Sat & Sun 11am – 4pm.

Jester House and Café

Coastal Highway • Tasman • 03 526 6742
lunch@jesterhouse.co.nz • www.jesterhouse.co.nz

Delicious handmade food served with a slice of paradise.

Enjoy tame eel feeding and our whimsical garden playground full of art.

Open: Summer, 7 days 9am - 5pm.
Winter, Thurs to Sun 9am - 4.30pm.
Closed public holidays.

Studio Woodturners

Ann & Bob Phillips

916 Coastal Highway 60 • Mapua • 03 540 2467
abphillips@clear.net.nz • www.nelsonarts.org.nz

Ann and Bob are internationally recognised artists and authors. Their beautifully designed works use native woods from sustainable sources and range from quality foodsafe domestic ware to unique art pieces.

Their idyllic coastal studio is open throughout summer and at other times by appointment.

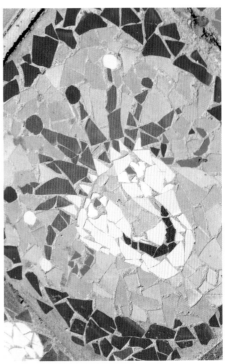

139

Rare Creations

Andreas Niemann

136 Aranui Rd • Mapua • 03 540 2225
andreas@rarecreations.co.nz
www.rarecreations.co.nz

Displaying the contemporary designs of Andreas Niemann and other New Zealand cabinetmakers, Rare Creations is the only dedicated fine furniture gallery in the region. All furniture meets the highest standards and finish, with a timeless quality that will appeal for generations to come. Many of the pieces at Rare Creations are made in the attached workshop.

Open: Mon, Tue, Thu and Fri 9am - 5pm, Wed 12pm - 6pm and Sat 10am - 1pm.

140A

Mike Perry

3 Toru Street • Mapua • 03 540 2420 • 021 0244 9667
mikeperry@paradise.net.nz

Mike's work has been described as a mixture of ceramics and mechanics.

Visit his studio in Mapua for an interesting experience.

140B

LAUGHING FISH STUDIO

OPEN

PRINTS
PAINTINGS
CERAMICS

By Shona McLean

140c

The Cool Store Gallery

7 Aranui Road • Mapua • 03 540 3778 • 021 562 782
info@coolstoregallery.co.nz
www.coolstoregallery.co.nz

The Cool Store Gallery represents over 150 artists and has a large jewellery collection.

Open: Summer, daily 11am - 5pm. Winter, Wed to Sun 11am - 4pm.

Laughing Fish Studio

Shona McLean

24 Aranui Road • Mapua • 03 540 3940
themtwo@laughingfishstudio.co.nz
www.laughingfishstudio.co.nz

Award winning artist Shona McLean and husband Martin Lindley produce unusual handmade ceramics, limited edition prints and original artwork from their vibrant, quirky studio.

Open: Most daylight hours over summer, reduced hours in winter. Visitors always welcome.

Lisa Chandler

60 Brabant Drive • Ruby Bay
03 540 3933 • 021 461 148
lisa@lisachandler.co.nz
www.lisachandler.co.nz

Winner Regional Art Awards 2007 - Landscape Seascape Section

Lisa Chandler is the fresh new face of representational art in Nelson, producing contemporary paintings of life and landscapes. She works with the canvas texture, dry-brushing to build up layers and create immediacy in her work. Lisa would love to welcome you to her gallery in stunning Ruby Bay. Please phone for an appointment.

Price Range: $495 - $2,000.

142

Playing with Fire

Darryl Frost

147 Kina Beach Road • Tasman • 021 983 808
darrylfrost@xtra.co.nz

From his anagama kiln and studio at Kina Beach, Darryl creates an eclectic range of award-winning wood-fired ceramic sculptures, wall panels, vases and smaller works, all featuring his signature sumptuous wood-ash glazes. His stunning sculpture garden creates a magnificent backdrop for his bold outdoor sculptures. With wine tasting across the road and the beach within walking distance, Playing with Fire is well worth the visit.

Open: Most days.

Pricing: From $50 to large scale commissions.

Kina Beach Vineyard

Dee Road • Kina Beach • 03 526 6252
kinabeach@xtra.co.nz • www.kinabeach.co.nz

Kina Beach is a single vineyard offering boutique style
wines - "the taste of our place."

The north-facing peninsular site produces grapes of
distinction. Leaf plucking, fruit thinning and harvesting
is all done by hand to ensure that each bunch reaches
its optimum ripeness and character. We combine this careful approach with Moutere's clay/gravel
soils, low rainfall and Nelson's famous sunshine hours to help craft multiple award-winning wines.

Open: All year by appointment.

The Old Schoolhouse Cottage offers romantic luxury accommodation amongst the vines.

Jane's Art Studio

Jane Smith

27 Goddard Road • Tasman • 03 526 6772
027 526 6772 • janeforart@hotmail.com

Jane is a watercolour artist. Her quirky sense of humour is reflected in her whimsical portrayal of generously proportioned folks and their everyday activities. Her ability to capture the humour in ordinary situations is often greeted with laughter as viewers relate to her colourful artworks.

Price range: $100 – $1,200.
Commissions are welcome.

Open: Most days Sep to May, please phone to visit during winter months

Outlets: Rutherford Gallery, Nelson.

Marion Towns

26 Baldwin Rd • Tasman • 03 526 6035 • 027 678 0093
artistnz@ihug.co.nz • www.mariontowns.co.nz

Marion creates vibrant pastel landscapes and nudes. Her studio/workshop features both indoor and outdoor art, and classes are available.

Open: Most days or by appointment.

Sue Newitt Pottery

173 Weka Road • Mariri • 03 526 6817
sue@celsoft.co.nz • www.nelsonpotters.co.nz

Sue creates simple forms from hand thrown, high fired translucent porcelain and celadon glazes. Her workshop is situated 2km from Tasman heading towards Motueka.

Outlets: South Street Gallery, RED Gallery and The Suter Art Gallery store, Nelson.

Open: Most week days 10am – 4pm or please phone.

Sealevel Studio
Sculpture Gallery

Tim Wraight, Che Vincent

Highway 60 • Tasman • 03 526 6712 • Tim 021 703 743
Che 027 721 8283 • sealevel@tasman.net
che@chevincent.co.nz • www.chevincent.co.nz

Set over the water on the Moutere Inlet, Sealevel Studio houses the workshops of sculptors Tim Wraight and Che Vincent, as well as a contemporary sculpture gallery. Tim's work in wood and other materials grace marae, public buildings and significant art collections, while Che sets new standards of skill with his work in metal. Both artists share a commitment to achieving artistic merit and technical excellence.

Open: Daily from 10am.

Redwood Valley and the mountains at sunset (above). Photo: Seifrieds Vineyard. Local olives (below). Photo: Nelson Mail

The Moutere

The Moutere is home to artists, handmade preserves, world class wineries, berries, lavender, handmade knives, apples, one of the country's most microscopic microbreweries, blackcurrants, an outdoor pursuits centre, olive oil, New Zealand's oldest pacifist community, a factory making cheese from sheep's milk and a place were you can stay in a teepee.

It's also where Braeburn apples were first grown. European settlement of the area began in 1843 and many of the area's original Pakeha (European) were German.

In the Neudorf Valley you'll find Tim and Judy Finn's world famous Neudorf Vineyards.

Whenever I visit Neudorf Vineyards, I think about how far the Finns and their wines have come. The place and their success are seductive testaments to the power of dreams, talent and commitment. They've also been fantastic supporters of the Moutere community and their biennial fundraiser, A Country Occasion is a brilliant event so picturesque it belongs in a movie. The next one will be on the last Sunday in November 2009.

Unlike some destinations, the Moutere rewards the curious. It's not like you turn up and everything is laid out for you to enjoy, you have to do a little snooping.

For an area synonymous with fine wine, it also has an admirable lack of pretentiousness and an authenticity that is very appealing.

147A

147B

Tracy Duncan

97 Carlyon Road • Mahana • 03 543 2090
027 543 2090 • mahanagrl@hotmail.com
www.tracyduncan.co.nz

Tracy Duncan is an award winning artist and illustrator, currently exploring concepts of identity and alienation. Her studio is open by appointment.

Anna Barnett

Sunrise Valley • RD1 • Upper Moutere • 03 543 2601
027 460 3039 • annabarnett@xtra.co.nz
www.nelsonpotters.co.nz

Anna's work is constantly evolving, with nature providing endless inspiration. Functional ware, Raku fired teapots, "Glaze Art" — creating abstract art with glaze, using richly textured surfaces. Anna also creates microscopic images and photographs them as abstract art.

Visitors welcome. Open: Most days 9am - 5pm. You are welcome to phone.

Moutere Store. Photo: Daniel Allen

Katie Gold & Owen Bartlett Pottery

1380 Main Road • Upper Moutere
03 543 2544 • katie_gold@paradise.net.nz

The Katie Gold and Owen Bartlett Pottery gallery is situated on an historic property nestled amongst spectacular gardens in Upper Moutere village. Here Katie creates colourful clay shoes and handbags as well as layered, wrapped and textured vessels and bowls, glaze printed with references to New Zealand's history and geography. Owen produces handmade limited edition lifestyle tableware including The Moutere Hills Harvest Collection.

Outlets throughout New Zealand. Open: Most days 10am – 5pm. Ring first if making a special trip.

Neudorf Vineyards

Neudorf Road • Upper Moutere • 03 543 2643
wine@neudorf.co.nz • www.neudorf.co.nz

Neudorf is considered one of New Zealand's top wineries. "Their wines are suffused with minerality and nervosite." *Robert Parker's Wine Advocate 2008.*

Discover what one of the worlds' most influential wine writers is talking about. Bring a picnic and linger. Producers of Pinot Noir, Chardonnay, Sauvignon Blanc, Riesling and Pinot Gris.

Cellar door open: Daily 11am – 5pm.

Neudorf Vineyards. Photo: Nelson Tasman Tourism

Michael MacMillan Sculptor

Workshop/Gallery

252 Neudorf Road • RD 2 • Upper Moutere • 03 543 2252
021 069 1407 • michaelmacmillan@xtra.co.nz
www.michaelmacmillan.co.nz

Michael is well known for his large outdoor sculptures and limited edition bronzes. His work is described as bold, reflective, textured, carved and kinetic. After 30 years of experience, Michael continues to develop his sculpture and push boundaries, incorporating ceramic, metals, bronze, resins and aggregate. Visit Michael in his workshop, stay in the exquisite country B&B accommodation and consider some of his sculpture for your home and garden.

Outlet: WOW® Museum, Nelson.

Viewing by appointment, commissions and enquiries welcome. Price Range: $350 – $50,000+

Photos: (top left) Gregory Crow and (middle right & bottom left) Nelson Mail

151

Neudorf Hall
Exquisite Country
Bed & Breakfast

Jackie Crow & Michael MacMillan

252 Neudorf Road • RD 2 • Upper Moutere
03 543 2252 • 021 157 6444
neudorfhall@xtra.co.nz • www.neudorfhall.co.nz

Hosts Jackie Crow and Michael MacMillan welcome you to experience European sophistication with luxurious rooms, an open fire, and rural views and vistas of Mount Arthur. Being just a short stroll to Neudorf Vineyards and Neudorf Dairy makes for a gastronomical, relaxing and memorable sojourn 35 minutes from Nelson.

One single and one double suite available. Gluten free and organic breakfast options.

Contact us for availability and pricing.

Anchorage Wines

Moutere Highway • 47 Flett Road • Lower Moutere
03 526 7252 • susie@anchoragewines.co.nz
www.anchoragewines.co.nz

Anchorage is owned and operated by the Drummond family, local entities since the 1800s. They produce a range of award winning wines from their vineyards in Riwaka, Motueka and the Moutere, and invite you to taste the full range at their Flett Road Cellar Door.

Cellar Door Open: Oct to Mar, Wed to Sun from 10am. Closed Christmas, Boxing and New Year's days.

Cooking with Angela Bone

Motueka River Lodge

1173 Motueka Valley Highway • Ngatimoti
03 526 8668 • enquiries@motuekalodge.com
www.motuekalodge.com

Foodies of all levels are invited to enjoy creative, informal, hands-on cooking classes in our stunning lodge kitchen. Contact the lodge for a full timetable, prices and further information.

Erika Aupperle

Maata Pottery

Motueka Valley Highway • Woodstock RD1 • Motueka
03 54 33620 • 021 0618 349 • anderi@ts.co.nz
www.nzpotters.com

Erika has been working with clay for many years, throwing, hand building or casting pots to hold, use or behold with pleasure every day. You will find Maata Pottery between Motueka and Tapawera, 1.5km past Woodstock Junction towards Motueka.

Outlets: Potters Patch, Motueka; Refinery Gallery, Nelson.

Open: Most days, please phone to confirm.

A Country Occasion, Neudorf Vineyard. Photo: Neudorf Vineyard

Photo (below): Marion van Dijk

Sightseeing

Sir Mountford Tosswill Woollaston KB (1910–1998) Old Hop Kiln, Upper Moutere 1976 (detail), watercolour and pencil on paper 475 x 580mm. Gifted by the artist in 1979. *The Suter Art Gallery Collection.*

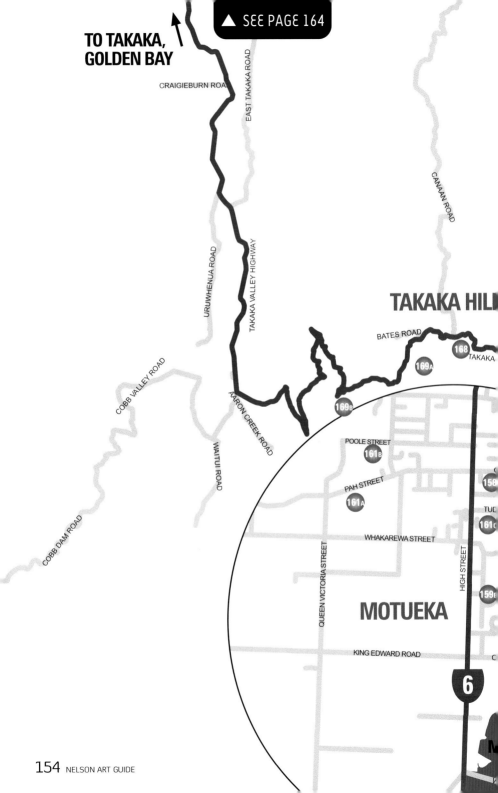

▲ SEE PAGE 164

TO TAKAKA, GOLDEN BAY

CRAIGIEBURN ROAD

EAST TAKAKA ROAD

CANAAN ROAD

URUWHENUA ROAD

TAKAKA VALLEY HIGHWAY

TAKAKA HIL

BATES ROAD

168 TAKAKA

169A

COBB VALLEY ROAD

AARON CREEK ROAD

169B

WAITUI ROAD

POOLE STREET

161B

158

PAH STREET

161A

TUD

161C

WHAKAREWA STREET

COBB DAM ROAD

QUEEN VICTORIA STREET

HIGH STREET

159B

MOTUEKA

KING EDWARD ROAD

6

Motueka & Abel Tasman National Park

161c TORRENT BAY

ABEL TASMAN NATIONAL PARK

MARAHAU HARVEY ROAD

MARAHAU VALLEY

MARAHAU

N

RIWAKA-SANDY BAY ROAD

6

KAITERITERI

LEY ROAD

163 RIWAKA KAITERITERI ROAD

MOTUEKA QUAY

60

MOTUEKA

TO MAPUA, RICHMOND, NELSON

159A

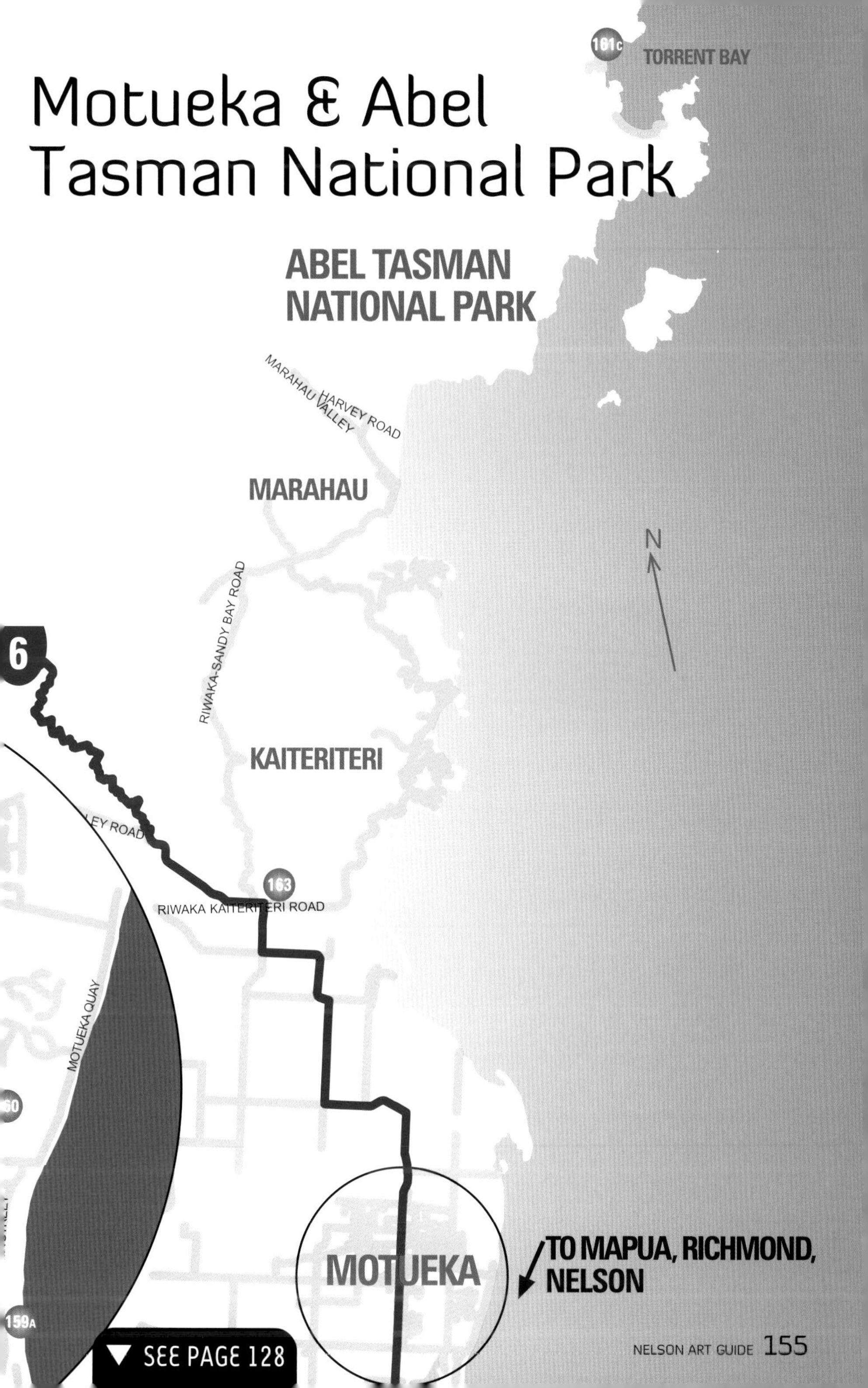

▼ SEE PAGE 128

Motueka

Motueka means 'Island of Bush with Weka' and in the 1960s it was a tobacco boom town. These days most people associate it with pipfruit, fishing, adventure tourism and hops. Talley's Fisheries are based in Motueka and the town is the gateway to the Abel Tasman National Park.

To the untrained eye Mot, as the locals call it, looks a lot like any New Zealand provincial town.

Look closer, though, and you'll find creativity bubbling away and an increasingly cosmopolitan community making the most of the superb climate and stunning natural environment.

One clue as to Motueka's cultural health is the way High Street's public seats and rubbish bins have been made by local artists. Another is the fact it has two cinemas - one of which, The Gecko Theatre, specialises in art-house movies from all over the world.

In 1985 The Loft Gallery opened in an old two storey shed next to where the Gothic Bar and Restaurant sits in High Street today.

The Loft championed Toss Woollaston's work and over the years showed a line up of artists that included renowned painters Philip Trusttum, Philip Clairmont, Bill Hammond and photographer Laurence Aberhart. No, you did not misread the last sentence: Woollaston, Trusttum, Clairmont, Hammond and Aberhart all exhibited in an old shed in Mot!

Part of the town's history that survives today is its historic salt water baths which can be reached through the Motueka Beach Reserve at the end of Wharf Road. A walk along the Motueka Sandspit is recommended for anyone interested in birdlife. The spit is one of the places the migratory godwits spend winter before starting their massive trip back to their nesting grounds in the Arctic Circle.

From Motueka it's a short jaunt to two beautiful spots: Kaiteriteri and Marahau. A visit to Marahau will give you a chance to check out the start of the renowned Abel Tasman National Park. You can walk in to the park from the car park, or take a launch, water taxi or kayak from the main beaches at Kaiteriteri or Marahau.

Someone who loves Motueka's proximity to other great spots is sculptor John Wolter of Wood Pigeon Studio who lives near Toss Woollaston's last residence in Riwaka. "Motueka is an amazing place – it's beautiful, relaxed and has got a great energy about it. It's the perfect environment for creating."

Hop Garden in Riwaka (below). Photo: Nelson Tasman Tourism
Opposite Page (top left) Janie Seddon on Motueka Quay. (top right,clockwise) Seat on High Street by Damien Stones & John Mutu, Split Apple Rock, Maori Carving by John Mutu & Tim Wraight and Sea Shell mural by Chris Finlayson & Liana Te'Aute. Photos: David Short. (middle left) The Gecko Theatre. Photo: The Gecko Theatre.

Motueka i-SITE Visitor Centre

20 Wallace St • Motueka • 03 528 6543 • info@motuekaisite.co.nz
www.motuekaisite.co.nz

Open every day for friendly and objective information on what to see, where to go and how to get there. Take advantage of our local expertise and free booking service for short trips or long adventures! We are happy to help create your personalised itinerary for transport, accommodation and activities.

Open: Oct to May weekdays 9am - 5.30pm, weekends 9am - 4.30pm. June to Sep weekdays 9am - 4.30pm, weekends 9am - 3.30pm.

Photo (below): Marion van Dijk

Sightseeing

Sir Mountford Tosswill Woollaston KB (1910-1998) Motueka Harbour 1970, oil on hardboard 995 x 1300mm. Presented by the Peter Stuyvesant Trust, London in 1971. *The Suter Art Gallery Collection.*

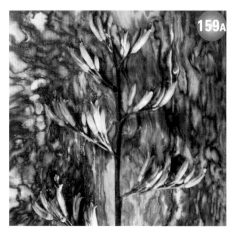

Verena Portmann

119 Trewavas Street • Motueka • 03 528 6735
verena.p@clear.net.nz

Verena blends and manipulates her photos, drawings and paintings to create a collage of textures and forms that express her connection with land and sea. Visit by appointment.

Motueka Wharf (above). Photo: Motueka Recreational Flight Training

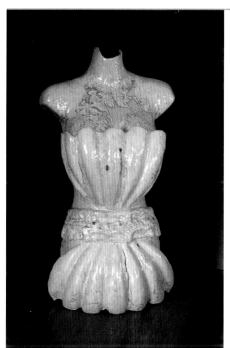

a.r.t Gallery and Framing

354 High Street • Motueka • 03 528 4970 • 027 213 4724

Located in one of Motueka's iconic 50s buildings, what was once a cordial factory is now a showcase of work from emerging and established artists throughout New Zealand. Gallery owner Melissa Floyd has her own distinctive crystalline glazed sculptural forms on display.

Open: Mon to Fri 10am – 5pm and Sat 10am – 12.30pm. Summer, Sat and Sun 10am – 4pm.

Copper Beech Gallery
John R Gatenby

240 Thorp Street • Motueka • 03 528 7456
021 256 0053 • john@copperbeechgallery.co.nz
www.CopperBeechGallery.co.nz

John Gatenby's paintings capture his strong affinity with nature, the land and sea.

His sensitivity for his subject is reflected in his meticulous attention to detail and his ability to capture its magnificence.

John welcomes commissions — these are an undertaking that takes time, patience and the consideration to incorporate images important to the client into his own vision.

He paints full time, using high grade acrylics on acid free, archive quality board.

John's gallery is situated in the grounds of his home where fine bed and breakfast accommodation is also offered.

Visitors are welcome at the gallery, which is usually open daily but if you're making a special trip, please phone to avoid disappointment.

Te Āwhina Marae

133 Pah Street • Motueka • 03 528 6061
fax 03 528 8995 • info@tam.org.nz • www.tam.org.nz

Te Āwhina Marae strives to embrace all people by offering hospitality, education and health services under the mana of Ngāti Rarua and Te Āti Awa. These services are open between Mon to Fri 8am - 5pm. If you wish to visit the Marae, please contact us first.

Sue Dasler Pottery

89 Poole Street • Motueka • 03 528 4080
suedasler@xtra.co.nz

Finely crafted contemporary ceramics.

Local outlets: South Street Gallery, Nelson; The Cool Store Gallery, Mapua.

Open: Most days, please phone to confirm.

Wilsons Abel Tasman

Meadowbank Homestead, Awaroa & Torrent Bay Lodge

265 High Street • Motueka • 03 528 2027 • 0800 223 582
info@abeltasman.co.nz • www.AbelTasman.co.nz

The Wilson family draws on seven generations of experience in the Nelson region to bring the fascinating history of the Abel Tasman National Park to life. Overnight beachfront lodge stays are available year-round and include walking, guided sea kayaking, Vista Cruise and Vigour Water Taxi options. Also specialising in single day options.

Winner of the New Zealand Tourism Awards 2006 Qualmark Mark of Quality.

Wood Pigeon Art Studio

John Wolter

39 Kaiteriteri Road • RD2 • Motueka • 03 528 6672
john@wolterartstudio.com • www.wolterartstudio.com

Most days, John can be found torch in hand with sparks flying around him at the aptly named Wood Pigeon Studio set against the beautiful Riwaka landscape.

Drawing on his training as a furniture maker, John utilises his talents in a variety of ways and is particularly known for his metalwork. His figurines with their outstretched poses and poignant stances often have an underlying narrative of their own and his richly coloured metal vessels boast both form and function.

One of the delightful things about a visit to Wood Pigeon Studio is that you never know what you might discover - painting, sculpture, a wall hanging, perhaps even a wood pigeon perched on the gate or immortalised as one of John's works.

Price range: $70 - larger commission pieces.
Open: Most days.

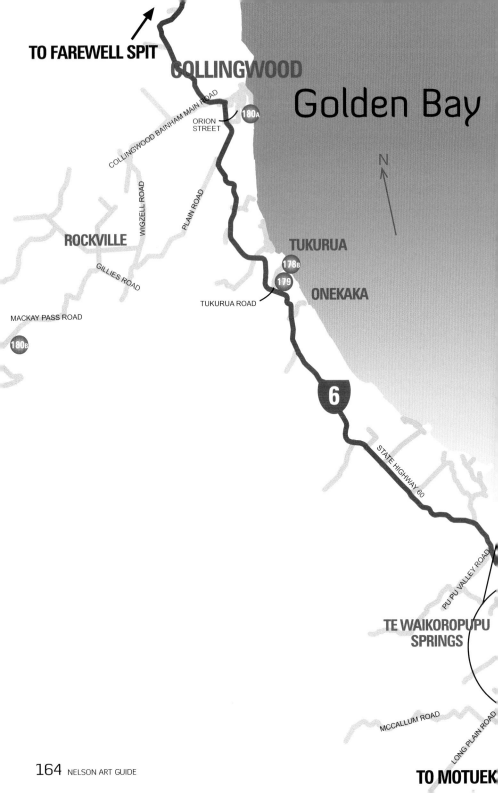

TO FAREWELL SPIT

COLLINGWOOD

Golden Bay

COLLINGWOOD BAINHAM MAIN ROAD

180A

ORION STREET

N

WIGZELL ROAD

PLAIN ROAD

ROCKVILLE

TUKURUA

GILLIES ROAD

178B

179

ONEKAKA

TUKURUA ROAD

MACKAY PASS ROAD

180B

6

STATE HIGHWAY 60

PU PU VALLEY ROAD

TE WAIKOROPUPU SPRINGS

MCCALLUM ROAD

LONG PLAIN ROAD

TO MOTUEK

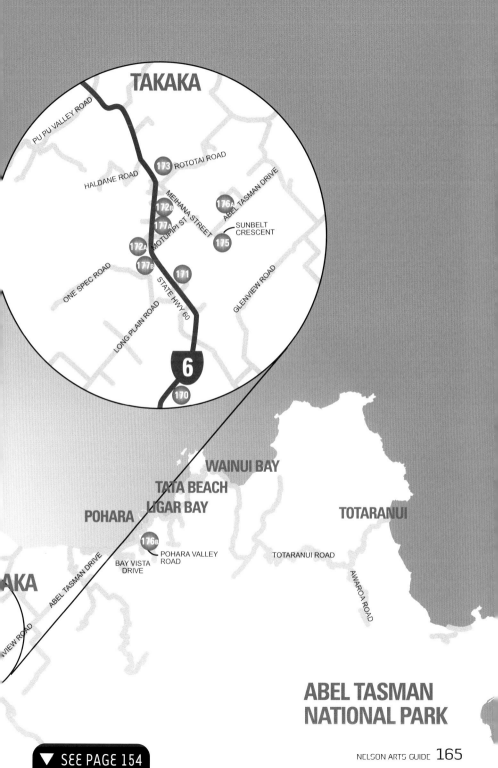

TAKAKA

PU PU VALLEY ROAD

173 ROTOTAI ROAD

HALDANE ROAD

MEIHANA STREET

172B

177

176A ABEL TASMAN DRIVE

SUNBELT
CRESCENT

MOTUPIPI ST STREET

172A

175

177B

ONE SPEC ROAD

171

GLENVIEW ROAD

STATE HWY 60

LONG PLAIN ROAD

6

170

WAINUI BAY

TATA BEACH

LIGAR BAY

POHARA

TOTARANUI

176B

POHARA VALLEY
ROAD

BAY VISTA
DRIVE

ABEL TASMAN DRIVE

AKA

TOTARANUI ROAD

AWAROA ROAD

VIEW ROAD

ABEL TASMAN
NATIONAL PARK

▼ SEE PAGE 154

Te Waikoropupu Springs. Photo: Nelson Tasman Tourism

Golden Bay

From the sweeping beauty of Farewell Spit and the golden sands of Tata Beach, to the wild magnificence of Wharariki Beach and the turquoise waters of Te Waikoropupu Springs, Golden Bay's beauty fills you up in the nicest of ways.

A word of advice – give yourself as much time in the bay as you can. Even Nelsonians who get over there every year fall into the trap of underestimating how much there is to enjoy in the bay. Looking at a map it can be tempting to try and cram all of its major sights into a couple of days, but it pays to give yourself enough time to savour the experience.

It is also worth taking your time getting to Golden Bay. Before you even get to the mighty Takaka Hill you might like to venture up the Riwaka Valley and have a dip in the chilly but crystal clear waters of the Riwaka Resurgence.

Heading over the hill you'll find a number of lookouts and walks on offer and on the plateau not far from the top you'll find sculptor Bruce Mitchell making art in splendid isolation. Bruce, who specialises in marble and granite, has been living up there for over 20 years and has no plans to leave. "It's the space. It has a nice outlook and it's not too crowded on the neighbour front," he says.

Golden Bay is consistently mentioned by international publications as one of the most desirable places on earth, and there's a good reason why.

Takaka itself is an easy-going, charming place. There are no traffic lights, no parking meters and only one cash machine. Yet the town boasts a cinema, several good places to eat, Schnapp Dragon Village Distillery, all the shops you need and the Wholemeal Café, which has been serving up good food and exhibiting art for 30 years.

"Laid-back to near-horizontal, Takaka is the business centre for the Golden Bay area, and the last town of much import as you head towards the South Island's northwest corner. The local community of rootsy artists and bearded, dreadlocked types rubs shoulders with hardened farmers and crusty fisherman in harmonious equilibrium: the bike shop sells guitar strings; the pub serves chai," says the Lonely Planet's latest edition.

Philly Hall, the owner of Monza Gallery on Commercial Street, says the art that comes out of Golden Bay reflects its natural environment. The fact it is surrounded by mountains and sea with only one road in and out plays a big part in its identity. "Anything that is not Golden Bay is 'over the hill'. It doesn't matter if it's London, LA or Motueka, it's all 'over the hill'," she laughs.

Just on from Takaka you'll find Collingwood, which was the first plastic-bag free town in New Zealand. It's also the departure point for tours to Farewell Spit and the Heaphy walking track in Kahurangi National Park. In maori Kahurangi means 'Treasured possession' and when you visit you will see why.

Central Takaka (top left) and Mural by Monique Richards (top right). Photos: Daniel Allen. Tata Beach (below) Photo:Spring Ursula Thomas

Bruce Mitchell

1449 State Highway 60 • Takaka Hill
027 310 5878 • rocknstone@xtra.co.nz

Bruce Mitchell offers a range of outdoor furniture, garden art and serious sculpture in local marbles.

The outdoor gallery exhibition site is open 9am - 5pm, Daily from mid January to mid March, other times by appointment. Look for the sign 200 metres past Bob's Lookout on the left when travelling to Takaka.

Commissions welcomed.

Photo (below): Marion van Dijk

Sightseeing

Marjorie Naylor (1908-1985), Golden Bay from Takaka Hill (c.1950), watercolour on paper 710 x 822mm. Bequeathed by the artist in 1985. *The Suter Art Gallery Collection.*

Archway Islands, Golden Bay. Photo: Nelson Tasman Tourism.

Dean Raybould

1936 State Highway 60 • Central Takaka • 03 525 9510
021 104 3588 • deanraybould@xtra.co.nz

Dean's works on possum skin, glass, wood, walls and canvas are spiced with social and environmental commentary, black humour and ambiguous musings on human existence. Flora, fauna, words and pattern all simmer in a cohesive collision of fine details and loose spontaneity.

Outlets: The Cool Store Gallery, Mapua; Harvest Gallery, Greytown; Art by the Sea Gallery, Auckland. Visit by appointment.

Beatrice Bourhis

Gallery Z

29 Main Road (SH 60) • Takaka • 03 525 7172 • 027 458 7172
be@bebou.co.nz • www.bebou.co.nz • www.eateryontherock.co.nz

Beatrice Bourhis' abstract mixed media paintings and collages are vibrant and playful. In her works on glass, perspex and metal she interweaves colours and textures to create works with great depth.

Gallery Z is located at Eatery on the Rock, please use restaurant car park.

Opening hours are flexible, please ring for information. Studio visits by appointment.

Beatrice's work is also available at Oriel Gallery, Picton.

172A

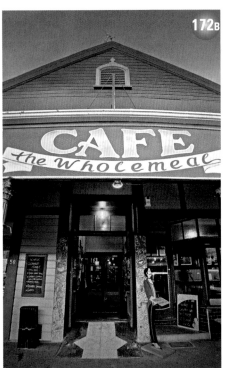

172B

Monza Gallery

More Outstanding New Zealand Art

25 Commercial Street • Takaka • 03 525 8510
phillyhall@xtra.co.nz • www.monza.co.nz

Delight in the creativity of Golden Bay at Monza Gallery. Artist Philly Hall and jewellers Nic Wooding and Jane Cassie are artists in residence, alongside an array of contemporary local art and jewellery on show in this historical setting.

Open: Daily, summer 10am - 5pm and winter hours vary.

Wholemeal Café

Commercial Street • Takaka • 03 525 9426
wholemealcafe@telstra.net.nz

Discover a café that combines innovative food, quality coffee, local art and a blend of many cultures in a small country town. Formerly the local theatre building, the café offers wonderful ambience, fusing the new with the traditional.

Robin Slow

9 Rototai Road • Takaka • 03 525 9213
r-slow.rototair@xtra.co.nz

Ko Parapara te maunga.

Ko Mohua te takiwā.

Ko Te Tai Tapu te moana.

Ko Te Waikoropupu te awa.

Ko Onetahua te marae.

Ko Te Ao Marama te whare.

Ko Robin Slow taku ingoa.

His works are images of the whenua (land) and from the land. They tell of the layers of footprints that have walked over the area of Mohua (Golden Bay) where he resides. Often painted in kokowai, soot and using gold leaf, the materials become part of the stories being expressed and though from a local perspective they have a universal meaning.

Artwork (top to bottom) Mohua, Pare - Tane and I te Po

InnerLight Studios

Spring Ursula Thomas

26 Sunbelt Crescent (cul-de-sac just off Abel Tasman Drive) or Eco Neighbourhood • Takaka • 03 525 7488
spring@innerlight.net.nz • www.innerlight.net.nz

InnerLight Studios is known for its sensitive, one of a kind portraiture and large custom photographs. Internationally award winning professional photographer Spring Ursula Thomas is an inspirational visual artist who examines the worlds of nature and spirit in her work. Her giclee on canvas images have a painterly quality and are often mistaken for contemporary oil paintings.

Visits by appointment. Commissions and documentary work welcomed.

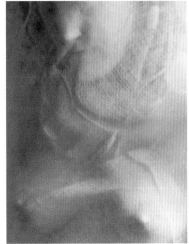

All photographs - Spring Ursula Thomas

176A

176B

Onetahua Marae

Pohara Valley Road • Pohara • 03 525 9484
fax 03 525 9068 • onetahuamarae@xtra.co.nz

A dream by the late Tui Martin, this marae was established for all people. With the hosts being Te Atiawa, Ngati Rarua, Ngati Tama and Mataa Waka.

Contact Vi Goodall on 03 525 9096 for more details.

Flax flower. Photo: Daniel Allen

Kathy Reilly

Shell Terrace • 124 Abel Tasman Drive • Takaka
03 525 8165 • kathy.reilly@xtra.co.nz
www.virtualbay.co.nz/kathyreilly

Kathy produces a range of paintings, etchings and pen and ink drawings from her studio overlooking the family dairy farm at Motupipi. A trained graphic designer, she produces works that offer a witty take on personal, political and social commentary.

Price range: $150 - $500. Visits by appointment.

Outlets: MONZA Gallery, Takaka; WOW® Museum, Nelson; Auckland Museum Store, Auckland.

177A

Schnapp Dragon Village Distillery

1 Hoddy Alley • Takaka • 03 525 9899
info@schnappdragon.co.nz
www.schnappdragon.co.nz

Schnapp Dragon Village Distillery create a distinctly Golden Bay range of citrus cellos, fruit liqueurs, honey/fruit wines, spirits and other local wines. Here you can sample and buy other locally-produced gourmet treats such as honey, coffee, chutney, salamis, cheese and organic breads made here in the distillery kitchen.

177B

Golden Bay i-SITE Visitor Centre

Willow Street • Takaka • 03 525 9136 • fax 03 525 9288
gb.vin@NelsonNZ.com

Golden Bay i-SITE puts you in the picture.

While you're in Golden Bay, come and talk to our knowledgeable staff. We'll make bookings for you and offer friendly, objective advice on things to see and do nearby and nationwide including activities, attractions, accommodation and transport.

178A

Photo (below): Marion van Dijk

Sightseeing

Doris Lusk (1916-1990) Onekaka Wharf 1969, watercolour, crayon and charcoal on paper 608 x 768mm. Presented by the Nelson Suter Art Society in 1998. *The Suter Art Gallery Collection.*

Sand Dunes, Farewell Spit (below). Photo: Nelson Tasman Tourism

178B

Gaya's Designs

Colours of the Sea Gallery

Tukurua Road • Tukurua • 03 524 8128
027 372 9818 or 027 276 3346
gaya@gayasdesigns.co.nz • www.gayasdesigns.co.nz

Gaya creates captivating New Zealand blue pearl jewellery that is displayed at Colours of the Sea Gallery alongside paintings, ceramics and fibre/fashion from other artists.

Next to Living Light Candles. Open: Most days.

Paul Winspear Pottery

Tukurua Rd • RD2 • Tukurua • 03 525 7965
winspalmer@clear.net.nz • www.nzpotters.com

Paul's work ranges from beautiful, affordable tableware to dramatic presentation pieces suitable as gifts or souvenirs. He creates his award-winning pieces using stunning contemporary glazes that reflect the vibrant colours of Golden Bay and traditional glazes with subtle earth tones. Paul has 30 years experience as a studio potter, has studied under respected potters and ceramists, and now teaches and mentors others.

Open: Summer (Dec to Apr) Daily 9am - 6pm (excluding statutory holidays). Winter please phone first.

Colin Coke

Arthaven Studio

3 Orion Street • Collingwood
03 524 8314 • colin@arthaven.co.nz
www.arthaven.co.nz

Colin creates colourful limited edition linocuts, inspired by the natural beauty of the Aorere Valley and Golden Bay. His hillside studio overlooking the Ruataniwha Inlet is located on the corner of Orion and Washington Streets, en route to the historic cemetery.

Open: Wed to Sun 9.30am - 5.30pm from mid-Dec to mid-April, or by appointment.

Reg Turner

Turner Studio Gallery

Mackay Pass Road • Rockville • 03 524 8717
regturner@xtra.co.nz • www.turnerreartist.co.nz

Reg's contemporary abstract paintings in oils and acrylics are inspired by the environment.

Enjoy boutique accomodation at Song of the Tui Lodge while viewing Reg's works. Follow the tourist signs to Heaphy Track, take the first road on left past Rockville Museum (MacKay Pass Road) and follow the signage to Song of the Tui Lodge.

Open: By appointment all year.

Wharariki Beach. Photo (above): Craig Potton

As you'll be discovering, there is an amazing range of people, art, food, scenery, wine, produce, beer, history, music and fun to be found in Nelson, Tasman and Golden Bay. There is definitely much more to explore and enjoy here than the average holiday allows so if you're nearing the end of yours, I think the only responsible thing to do is book another - don't you?

Have a good one!

Matt Lawrey

Farewell Spit Lighthouse (above) and Tata Beach, Golden Bay. Photos: Spring Ursula Thomas

The Cool Store Gallery, Mapua (above). Photo: Daniel Allen

Shop Around

The following artists are represented at galleries throughout the region, but do not have open studios.

Mike Hindmarsh

03 545 7180 • michaelhindmarsh@paradise.net.nz
www.mikehindmarsh.com

Mike Hindmarsh produces stylish, award winning contemporary furniture. His designs are hand crafted with thorough attention to detail.

Please contact Mike directly for commissions.

Outlets: Coastal Merchant, Nelson; The Cool Store Gallery, Mapua.

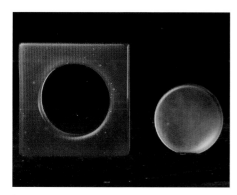

Lynette Cain

03 545 8288 • 027 282 7649

Lynette uses cast glass to create small-scale object art that reflects on the relationship between memories and culture and evokes a sense of connection.

Available locally at RED Gallery, Nelson.

Also available Oriel Gallery, Picton; Morgan Street Gallery and Flagstaff Gallery, Auckland.

David Foulds

03 547 7772 • 021 133 6304 • dfoulds@ihug.co.nz
www.dfoulds-artist.co.nz

A member of the Nelson Suter Art Society, David aims to create a sense of peace, tranquility and familiarity in his paintings. Artworks available through his online gallery and The Suter Art Gallery. Visits and commissions welcomed by appointment.

Isaac Ibbotson & Kim Stark

03 545 6468 • 021 847 222
workshop@mintgallery.co.nz • www.mintgallery.co.nz

Isaac and Kim are renowned for their distinctive wedding and engagement rings, investment pieces and collectables. Commissions welcomed.

Available through their online gallery and The Cool Store Gallery, Mapua; Inform, Christchurch; Gallery 33, Wanaka; Lure, Dunedin and Quoil, Wellington.

Jewels Vine

Nelson • 021 0295 1143 • info@jewelsvine.com
www.jewelsvine.com

Jewels Vine works with silver, gold and exotic materials to create a tiny world of unique pieces to be worn and treasured for life.

Available online and at Inform, Christchurch; Gallery 33, Wanaka and Quoil, Wellington. Price range: $50 - $1,000.

Phill Krammer

021 467 177 • phill@phillkrammer.co.nz
www.phillkrammer.co.nz

A designer and artist, Phill creates colourful, mystical dreamscapes that reference New Zealand scenery.

His paintings have a spacious, serene quality and are filled with texture and emotion.

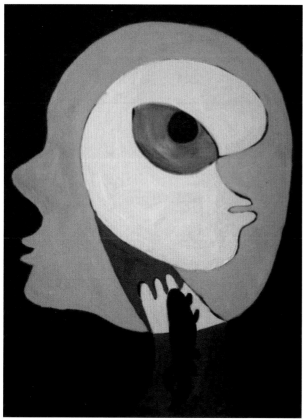

Peta Wright

03 546 8599 • 027 204 5978
petawright@xtra.co.nz
www.petawright.co.nz

Peta's quirky, colourful and unforgettable paintings are created in response to everyday life. Her pieces are full of charm, movement and imagination, and always include her pet dachshund.

Peta's paintings inspired by The Beatles were published and sold by Amazon.

Open air theatre, Trafalgar Street. Photo: Daniel Allen

Events

There's nothing the arts community likes more than a good party. From the fun-filled Port Nelson Mask Parade that kicks off the annual Nelson Arts Festival in October, to jazz concerts in the parks and vineyards, Nelson always celebrates in style. Local event managers regularly employ artists for entertainment, theming and performances for a range of events.

January

Sealord Nelson Summer Festival
December–February

Two months of free or low cost events in the region over summer. The Sealord Nelson Summer Festival starts just before Christmas with the fabulous family fun of the Community Trust Lantern Spectacular, and carries on right through until Sealord Opera in the Park. This festival aims to entertain locals and visitors with events mainly aimed at families who like a bit of fun.
www.nelsonfestivals.co.nz

Woollaston Nelson Jazzfest

The annual Jazzfest has become an integral part of summertime in Nelson. The reasons are simple – loads of sunshine, world-class musicians and the festival is packed with lots of events over five days, including concerts, park events, master classes and performances.
www.nelsonjazzfest.co.nz

Bayleys Twilight Art Markets

Held every Friday evening December to February, top of Trafalgar Street. A wide variety of paintings, sculptures, ceramics and jewellery as well as great performances. Held rain or shine!
www.nelsonart.info

Adam Festival of Chamber Music

The Adam Festival presents classical and contemporary music played by outstanding musicians from New Zealand and overseas. The concerts are staged in wonderful venues in Nelson City and beyond.
www.music.org.nz

Nelson Summer Kite Festival

The annual Nelson Summer Kite Festival held in Neale Park is the longest running kite festival in New Zealand. The festival attracts top kite fliers with amazing kites from around the world.
www.kites-rainbowflight.co.nz

Street Beat

Take a stroll through the city and do some people-watching among the summer crowds, to the sound of music from local musicians and guests. Performances at the top of Trafalgar Street and roving theatre acts.
www.nelsonjazzclub.co.nz

February

Sarau Festival - Moutere Community Centre

This blackcurrant festival is a fun packed day of festivities including a Farmers Market with art and produce.
www.saraufestival.co.nz

February (continued)

Sealord Nelson Summer Festival
See January for details.

Opera in the Park
A wonderful opportunity for people to experience a world class operatic concert in the relaxed setting of New Zealand's sunshine capital.
www.nelsonfestivals.co.nz

Bayleys Twilight Art Markets
See January for details.

Brightwater Wine & Food Festival
Featuring local wines, olive products and boutique beers, complemented with selected craft stalls. Quality food is provided by some of Nelson's best restaurants and cooking demonstrations are offered by internationally-recognised chefs. Set amidst vineyards and native bush. A great family day out.
www.bwff.co.nz

Festival of Opportunities
New Zealand's largest health and lifestyle festival has spectacular stalls showcasing healers and health products, jewellery, clothing and more. Free lectures and workshops, national and international speakers, plus food stalls and live entertainment.
www.nelsonhealthfest.co.nz

Nouveau Design Awards Fashion Show
The Nouveau Design Awards is an avante-garde fashion show that also provides scholarships for local secondary school students. Held at Spring Grove Drill Hall, Wakefield.
www.nouveaudesign.info

March

The Seresin Estate Antique & Classic Boat Show
Clinkers, canoes, classic sail boats, runabouts, classic hydroplanes and race boats, steam launches and old fibreglass boats come together for two days of boating, displays, talk and the odd race. Held at - St Arnaud, Nelson Lakes.
www.nzclassicboats.com

Fiona Pears performing at the Woollaston Jazzfest (below). Photo: Nelson Mail

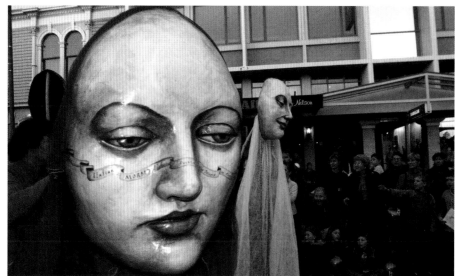

Port Nelson Masked Parade & Carnivalle (above). Photo: Nelson Mail

March (continued)

Mapua Easter Fair

More than 280 stalls from around New Zealand selling a variety of arts, crafts, plants and gourmet foods. Live entertainment. A fantastic fun day for everyone. Held at Mapua Domain.
www.mapua.school.nz

April

Dancesport Nelson - Easter Championship & Festival

Two full days of top class dance sport - ballroom, latin, and new vogue, featuring dancers of every age from all over New Zealand and a 'show spectacular' on both Saturday and Sunday evenings. Held at the Tafalagar Centre, Nelson.
www.dancesportnelson.co.nz

June

Founders Book Fair

A nine-day event held over Queen's Birthday weekend and the following week, at Founders Heritage Park.

Dedicated volunteers work all year categorising well over 50 tonnes of books preparing for the Founders Book Fair. This is Founders Heritage Park's annual fundraising event.
www.nelsonfestivals.co.nz

July

Nelson School of Music Winter Festival

Outstanding music, comedy and theatre with national and international artists makes winter a festive time in Nelson.

All performances are held at Nelson School of Music in Nile Street.
www.nsom.ac.nz

July (continued)

Blessing of the Fleet

An annual event to remember fishers lost at sea, to bless the fishing fleet and to celebrate the importance of the fishing industry to this region. Held at Sunderland Marine Pier on the waterfront at Wakefield Quay.

www.nelsonfestivals.co.nz

August

Ecofest

All the latest environmental-friendly ideas and information showcased over two days. Includes workshops and tours.

www.ecofestnelsontasman.co.nz

September

The Nelson International Film Festival

Up to 30 national and international films selected from other festivals around New Zealand are shown at the State Cinema.

www.nzff.co.nz

October

Nelson Arts Festival

Nelson welcomes spring with an explosion of creativity, for 12 days around Labour Weekend. Theatre, music, dance, sculpture, literary launchings, street and community events. The festival opens with thousands thronging central city streets for the Port Nelson Masked Parade and Carnivale.

www.nelsonfestivals.co.nz

Collingwood Street, Trolley Derby (below). Photo: Nelson Mail

NMIT Graduates Exhibition at The Suter Art Gallery (above). Photo: Nelson Marlborough Institute of Technology

Isel in Bloom

A fun day for everyone at Isel Park. Craft and food stalls, children's fun, live entertainment and a chance to see the mature gardens and historic Isel House in Main Road Stoke.
www.nelsonfestivals.co.nz

November

NMIT Visual Arts Graduates Degree Exhibition

New talent is on show at The Suter Art Gallery each year as graduates from the Diploma of Art and Design and the Bachelor of Visual Arts display their artworks from the year.
www.nmit.ac.nz

Broadgreen Historic House Rose Day

An annual craft fair celebrating beautiful Samuels Rose Gardens and Broadgreen Historic House. A relaxed family day held on sweeping lawns set with heritage trees, in Nayland Road.
www.nelsonfestivals.co.nz

A Country Occasion

A picturesque event held at Neudorf Vineyard. There are stalls and entertainment throught the grounds. Staples include quince, chuckney, chocolate and wild pork sandwiches. A community Fundraiser that is held biannually, the next is the last Sunday in November 2009.

December

Sealord Nelson Summer Festival

See January for detail.

Bayleys Twilight Art Markets

See January for detail.

For current information take a look at
www.nelsonnz.com/events

Nelson Arts Festival

www.nelsonartsfestival.co.nz

Welcome the spring with an explosion of creativity. The Nelson Arts Festival offers Nelsonians and visitors 12 days of top national and international theatre, dance, cabaret, music and talks packed around Labour Weekend (mid October). From dance and music on city streets to poetry in the vineyard it's a festival that celebrates the best in the arts while retaining a community focus — many events are free for families. World class events in Nelson's lovely heritage venues, book online when the programme comes out in August.

Photos: (top) Port Nelson Masked Parade, (top left) Pet Art Wear and Sculpture (right) Nic Moon

Adam Chamber Music Festival

www.music.org.nz

"... unbeatable" - NZ Listener, Best of 2007

For two weeks every two years the Adam Chamber Music Festival makes Nelson an exclusive and international focal point of fine music. Leading performers from New Zealand and overseas join the New Zealand String Quartet, the festival's ensemble-in-residence, in bringing you the best of classical music in a delightful environment.

For information about the next Adam Chamber Music Festival go to www.music.org.nz

Photos: (top to bottom) New Zealand String Quartet, Piers Lane, Pražák Quartet & David Tanenbaum

Woollaston Nelson Jazzfest

Nelson Jazz Club Inc

---
03 547 7211 • info@nelsonjazzfest.co.nz • www.nelsonjazzfest.co.nz
---

Now an integral part of summertime in Nelson, 2 – 6 January, the Woollaston Nelson Jazzfest offers a choice of more than 70 events over five consecutive days. Well-known New Zealand and international acts perform alongside local bands in parks and commercial venues throughout Nelson and Tasman. The Jazzfest launches with a free public concert at Fairfield Park.

Park events are held in Nelson, Richmond and Takaka. Venue performances in Nelson, Richmond, Mapua and Upper Moutere. Street performances in Nelson.

Ticket sales for concerts commence in November, check the website for details.

Nelson Winter Festival

Nelson School of Music • 48 Nile Street, Nelson
03 548 9477 • nsom@nsom.ac.nz
www.nsom.co.nz

Nelson School of Music presents ten days of outstanding concerts featuring international, New Zealand and Nelson artists.

The Nelson Winter Festival is launched with an opening party and offers something for everyone — from rock to classical music, dancing to cabaret, children's performances and matinee shows.

The auditorium is a preferred concert venue where exciting events are hosted year-round.

Call into the historic Nelson School of Music today to find out what's on, or check on the website www.nsom.co.nz.

A Word from the Mayors

The Nelson Region has long been a hotspot for creativity. The birthplace of WearableArt™ and inspiration for some of New Zealand's foremost painters — John Gully and Sir Toss Woollaston to name but two. Maybe it's the sunshine, maybe it's the wine, maybe the incomparable beaches and scenery — probably all three, but here in Nelson you can relax and let the creative juices flow.

Nelsonians are justifiably proud of the artists and craft practitioners living and working here and as a community we strongly support their endeavours. We have worked with our neighbours in Tasman to develop a regional approach to our support of the arts. This will continue to ensure a positive creative future that will cement art firmly into the fabric of our lives. We are building on the solid base of our heritage keeping alive the visions of our forefathers who built our art gallery - The Suter Art Gallery, the Nelson School of Music and the Theatre Royal.

Art reflects who we are as a city and a region, it tells our stories, captures our feelings and brings the community together.

Kerry Marshall
Mayor, Nelson City

Tasman District has nurtured creative souls for generations. Today we still appreciate the things that make Tasman such a special place to live and do business - long, balmy summer evenings or crisp winter mornings heralding an endless clear blue sky.

Dotted across the district are artists' studios where visitors are welcomed and can experience the inspiration that drives this creativity. Our entire community celebrates the arts with festivals and events and our council supports and encourages this.

As Mayor I value the integration of art into our everyday lives. Seeing creativity incorporated into our infrastructural work brings the process full circle.

I am proud to be Mayor in a community where we nurture the environment and leave our mark with aesthetic integrity. To me it demonstrates that we value the people and appreciate our place in the world.

Richard Kempthorne
Mayor, Tasman District

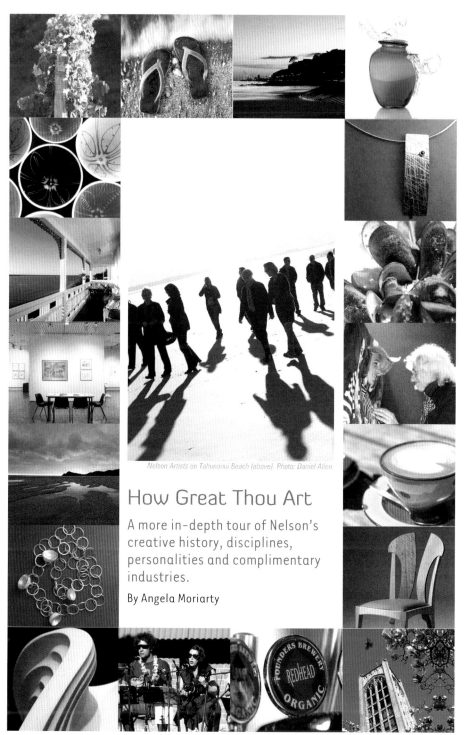

Nelson Artists on Tahunanui Beach (above). Photo: Daniel Allen

How Great Thou Art

A more in-depth tour of Nelson's creative history, disciplines, personalities and complimentary industries.

By Angela Moriarty

Once Upon A Time...

The following timeline offers a snapshot of Nelson's creative history and documents some of its turning points. What's next? Time will tell. *Illustrations by Dean Raybould.*

About 800

Polynesian voyagers first arrived in this area aboard the Uruao Waka.

1842

First European settlers arrive in Nelson.

1867

Bishop Suter and his wife Amelia move to Nelson and soon become leading figures in the city's early cultural life.

1895

Bishop Suter passes away. Amelia realises her husband's dream by gifting land, money and art as the founding donation for The Suter Art Gallery.

1642

Isaac Gilseman draws 'Abel Tasman's Bay' in the ship's journal during the explorer's visit to Tasman Bay.

1840s

Charles Heaphy and William Fox recorded the settlement of Nelson in watercolour.

1883

Nelson Suter Arts Society is established.

1899

The Suter Art Gallery - built as a memorial to Andrew Burn Suter, Bishop of Nelson from 1865-1885 – opens.

1950s

Nelson's clay resources draw pioneering potters such as Mirek Smisek and later Harry and May Davis to Nelson.

1960s

Jack and Peggy Laird arrive and set up Waimea Pottery, a craft pottery workshop near Richmond where they offered apprenticeships for young studio potters.

1970s

Boom period for ceramic art. Motueka Pottery Workshop, Nelson Community Potters, Craft Potters Nelson and the Nelson Potters Association are all formed.

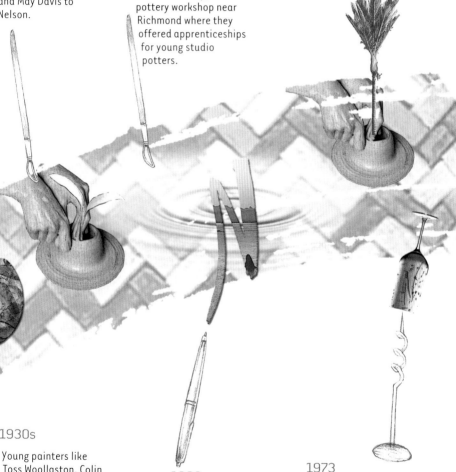

1930s

Young painters like Toss Woollaston, Colin McCahon and Doris Lusk begin drawing on their experiences in the region.

1969

The Nelson Provincial Arts Council (NPAC) is established to support emerging artists.

1973

Nelson's largest vineyard, Seifried, is established when Hermann and Agnes Seifried plant grapes in the Moutere Valley.

1976

First professional director of The Suter Art Gallery, Austin Davies is appointed.

1979

Painter Sir Mountford Tosswill (Toss) Woollaston is knighted.

1987

First of what is now known as the World of WearableArt™ Awards is held as a fundraiser in a small art gallery at Spring Grove.

1989

Royce McGlashen is made a member of the NZ Order of Merit for services to pottery.

1978

Fundraising mission enables extensive modernisation of The Art Suter Gallery.

1984

Ola & Marie Höglund move to Nelson and set up the now international renowned Höglund Art Glass.

1986

Steve Fullmer wins the Premier Earthenware Fletcher Brownbuilt Potter Award (also joint winner in 1987).

1993

Nelson Bays Arts Advocacy and Marketing Trust is established.

1994

First edition of the Nelson Regional Guide Book is produced.

1997

Jane Evans is made an officer of the NZ Order of Merit for services to painting.

2004

Dan Hennah wins an Oscar for set decoration for the Lord of the Rings film The Return of the King. It was Dan's third nomination for the award.

2008

Seventh edition of the Nelson Art Guide published.

1995

First Nelson Arts Festival.

1995

Gael Montgomerie, wins the inaugural National Association of Woodturners' top award, the Blue Cross.

1995

Whakatu Marae wharenui (meeting house) Kaakati is opened with carvings depicting the stories of six iwi and carved by a team lead by Mark Davis.

2004

Christine Boswijk is made an officer of the NZ Order of Merit for services to ceramic art.

Anne Rush is made a member of the NZ Order of Merit for services to the arts, including her role in establishing Nelson Bays Arts Marketing.

Ceramics

One of the ceramic artist's great goals is to enrich people's lives beyond the manufactured.

There's something about sipping from a handmade cup, or dining from a crafted bowl, that makes a drink or meal taste that little bit nicer.

Nelson is considered the centre of ceramics in New Zealand. The region's clay resources drew in pioneering potters Mirek Smisek and Harry and May Davis in the 1950s, with Jack and Peggy Laird setting up Waimea Pottery in the 1960s. The craft pottery workshop became a training ground for the likes of Royce McGlashen, Paul Laird and Charles Shaw.

Many local potters continue to be leading lights nationally, and some internationally. Ceramic artists can be found scattered all over the region and most welcome visitors to their workshops and galleries.

The Nelson Potters Association organises a major annual exhibition at The Suter Art Gallery each summer, along with themed exhibitions throughout the year.

As well as refering to the listings in this guide, those particularly interested in ceramics should pick up a copy of the free Nelson Potters map or visit South Street Gallery (see page 61), which features work from a large range of local potters. Or visit www.nelsonpotters.co.nz.

Kindly sponsored by Nelson Potters Association

Artworks (left to right, top to bottom) Anna Barnett, Sue Dasler, Owen Bartlett, Hugh and Saralinda MacMillan, Shona Mclean and Martin Lindley, Darryl Frost, Ralph Hetzel, Charles Shaw, Paul Winspear, Sue Newitt, Royce McGlashen & Paul Laird.

Opposites Attract

They say opposites attract and when it comes to their ceramic art, husband and wife team, Owen Bartlett and Katie Gold couldn't be more different.

Owen works in domestic ware and muted tones, while Katie's sculptural pieces are famous for their vibrant colours.

"It's quite good because we're not in competition," says Owen. "I'm just as happy when Katie's work sells as although we are separate businesses, all the funds end up in the Bartlett/Gold lifestyle charity!"

Owen trained "on the inside" with potters Royce McGlashen and Peter Gibbs, learning the trade in their production studios. Katie, on the other hand, was schooled in craft design at what is now known as the Nelson Marlborough Institute of Technology, experimenting in different media before falling for clay.

"I enjoyed clay because it was endless – I was fascinated that it seemed to have infinite possibilities."

Other media still influence her work, with a background in screen printing and weaving evident in the imagery and layering used in her forms.

The couple, who met through the Nelson Potters Association, set up their home gallery together in Upper Moutere in 2000. They are quick to hail the strong community of ceramic artists in the region.

"There are some of the world's top potters in Nelson," says Owen. "We also have some of the best clay work in the world within 10 minutes' drive."

Photos: Katie Gold bowl (above) & Owen Bartlett and Katie Gold in their studio (below)

Painting

"The landscape that enticed John Gully, frustrated Toss Woollaston, challenged Colin McCahon or captivated Sarah Greenwood, this fringe of mountains, coast and sapphire sea, has a very special place in the story of New Zealand painting." - *Graeme Stradling*

When Isaac Gilseman drew Abel Tasman's Bay in the ship's journal during Tasman's visit to Nelson in 1642, he made the first marks in a tradition of western art in New Zealand that continues today. This very early Nelson drawing describes hills, inlets, mountains and sea with an eye for information and beauty.

Adventurous young painters – the likes of Toss Woollaston, Colin McCahon and Doris Lusk – were inspired by the region's physical beauty. From the mid 1930s this group became the dominant force in New Zealand painting, basing much of their work on their time around the Nelson region.

Nelson's top painters and printmakers have earned the respect of discerning fine art buyers, creating a demand for their work. Painters such as Austin Davies, Sally Burton and Brian Strong have found both national and international demand, drawing art lovers to the region.

Generations of painters now follow in their footsteps, many of whom are graduates of the Nelson Marlborough Institute of Technology's School of Arts. The region has a long history of excellence in the arts, and a history of Nelson painters reads like a who's who of New Zealand art.

Kindly sponsored by the Nelson Regional Economic Development Agency

Artwork: Sally Burton painting detail (above) & Austin Davies in his studio (below). Photo: Daniel Allen

Dean Raybold in his studio (left) & painting in progress (detail). Photos: Daniel Allen

Illustrating the Facts

Golden Bay painter Dean Raybould is a master of visual and verbal puns, planting seeds of irony and opinion throughout the field of his work.

Also a commercial illustrator, Dean uses finely detailed imagery, abstract typography and verbal wit to give physicality to his social and environmental commentary.

Describing his style as 'haphazard', Dean works spontaneously rather than with focused consideration.

"It's a bit like writing a song — you don't really know where it's going to come from."

Describing himself as a 'border-line cynic', Dean's paintings are riddled with dark humour.

"Humour's a good way of getting under people's radar with serious issues and I naturally tend to see the funny side of things — even when they're not very funny" he laughs.

As well as large canvas works, Dean uses cut out wood for his paintings.

"The idea behind the cut out pieces is that the wall becomes the background — in a way I'm being lazy because I don't have to paint a background."

New Zealand born, Dean grew up in Australia from the age of 6. After returning to his homeland some 13 years ago, his work became strongly influenced by local issues and cultural icons.

"I like taking iconic things and messing with them a bit."

Anne Rush with Arum; a white room installation at The Suter Art Gallery. Photo: Daniel Allen

Mixed Media

By nature, artists are always looking for new things: new techniques, new views and new materials become part of the mix. The environment in which they live is the ultimate mixed media work, with inspirational colours, textures and materials.

Many artists who started their career as a painter of acrylics or oils, find their creative journey takes them so far that one medium no longer describes their work.

These people choose to build a variety of media into their works, applying new depth, layers and shapes.

Spoilt for choice, a mixed media artist must choose carefully, says Anne Rush.

"As an artist who works in mixed media I am offered infinite possibilities in the selection of material and technique to create artworks.

"The challenge for me is the discipline to select, create and sustain a personal artistic vocabulary that has integrity, context and meaning."

Anna Leary with Spring, 90 Days Tasman Bay on Tahunanui Beach. Photo: Tim Cuff.

Into the Mix

Like her work, Anna Leary's use of media is diverse.

A set of drawers in her Queens Road studio are filled with an artist's 'treasures': feathers collected from walks on the beach, flowers dried and pressed from friend's gardens, or textural papers salvaged from specially wrapped gifts.

As well as layering materials into her paintings on board, Anna paints onto a range of formed supports in wood and acrylic devised in collaboration with her engineering father.

"Utilising mixed media starts with ideas — then you've got to figure out how to realise them," says Anna.

"Often ideas link and build on each other, taking you with them."

They say one man's trash is another man's treasure, and Anna enjoys that a significant physical connection is built into the paintings she creates on pieces salvaged from demolition sites.

"I like the idea of finding beauty in the unexpected."

Jewellery

Bold jewellery with chunky settings, hand-hammered finishes, and clean lines have become one of Nelson's creative signatures.

Nelson has long been a seeding ground for contemporary New Zealand jewellery.

The creative journey started with the late Jens Hansen. Some of our leading jewellers spent their formative years under Hansen's guidance.

In recent years the jewellers have come together to foster their development in a group called Klustre. The annual Klustre exhibition, held around the time of the spring Nelson Arts Festival, is an excellent showcase of the diverse talents of established and emerging jewellers. Klustre's first show, in 2000, was the largest collaborative jewellery exhibition of its kind to be shown in Nelson and set an inspiring standard.

Expect to find a range of media and techniques, including beadwork, forged goblets, brooches in silver and gold, enamelling, greenstone, bone and paua shell. Jewellery studios and workshops can be found throughout Nelson City and beyond, and a number of top jewellers also have stalls at the Nelson Saturday Market.

Kindly sponsored by Jens Hansen Workshop

Kluster Jewellers (left to right, top to bottom) Zoe Buchanan, Gaya Selder, Andrea Barton, Ashley Hilton, Liz Kendrick, Zoe Buchanan, Claire Allain, Peter Elsbury & Mieke Van Dam

Lord of the Rings

While many Nelson artists have received international acclaim over the years, it was the selection of a Nelson jeweller to create The One Ring for Peter Jackson's Lord of the Rings film trilogy that cast the region's creative sector in its first global leading role.

Celebrated as one of the first avante-garde jewellers in New Zealand, the late Jens Hansen actually turned the job down when first approached to create the prototype for the world's most famous ring. His mind was changed just a few hours later at the urging of his sons Halfdan and Thorkild, both great fans of the books.

"It would be fair to say I said something along the lines of 'What, are you crazy, of course we should do it'," recalls Halfdan, who now runs the Selwyn Place workshop.

Jens' influence falls far beyond the One Ring.

Known as a bold, gregarious character, his workshop was a hub of experimentation and creative brilliance, attracting aspiring gold and silversmiths from around the globe.

Judith Taylor, curator of The Jeweller's Mark: The Jens Hansen Workshop Story, described the workshop as a place "where creativity and sociability were essential ingredients."

"His passion and commitment helped to advance the vibrant and confident spirit in the Nelson arts scene. His influence resonates in the creative life of Nelson, as well as in the work of many jewellers spread far and wide."

The One Ring, created for the Lord of the Rings film trilogy (above) & Jens Hansen (below). Photos: Jens Hansen Workshop

Sculptures (left to right, top to bottom) Michael MacMillan, Grant Palliser, Tim Royall & Darryl Frost

Sculpture

Enriching your environment with works of art allows communities to reflect on their past, present and future.

Public sculpture captures moments in time, offering cultural windows to future generations. It also offers artists the opportunity to extend their creativity; pushing their boundaries in scope, interpretation and media.

Throughout the listings in this book, you'll find reference to a number of the public works either commissioned by the local councils or gifted to the community by patrons. Around Nelson city you will find reference to several public works by Grant Palliser. The Tahunanui waterfront also features a trail of works relating to the region's settler and maritime heritage.

To view an impressive private collection of sculptural works visit Woollaston Estates winery at Mahana, which features pieces by some of Nelson and New Zealand's top sculptors. Sculpture enthusiasts should also stop off at Tim Wraight's dedicated sculpture gallery Sealevel Studio in Tasman, and Darryl Frost's Playing with Fire in Kina.

Christine Boswijk outside her workshop. Photo: Daniel Allen

Breaking the Mould

Christine Boswijk credits "visionary" patrons with paving her creative journey from domestic ware ceramicist to full time sculptor.

"The people that commission me to do things give me the opportunity to keep moving forward and have forays into the unknown. It's a very exciting, stimulating and challenging way to work."

Without this affirmation and investment, Christine, who was made a member of the NZ Order of Merit for services to ceramic art in 2004, says she would have been much more creatively timid.

"The signature works that I have done have all happened when people have noticed what I'm doing and have challenged me to do more and better."

While working in larger forms has seen Christine introduce new media into her works, clay is still very much her creative companion.

"I love the whole alchemy of working in clay. I love that you take a seemingly inert material, you breathe life into it, you put it into the fire, and it becomes rock. Every mark you put into it is there for infinity."

Woodwork (left to right, top to bottom) Nigel Whitton, Anne & Bob Phillips, David Haig and Roger Davies

Woodwork & Furniture

As well as exploring new methods, Nelson's woodworkers often merge established tradition and contemporary design — offering a modern take on an ancient art form.

Many of the techniques, skills, and solutions used in woodworking have barely changed for thousands of years. As they say, if ain't broke, don't fix it.

In addition to furniture making, there is a significant local tradition of wood carving in the Nelson region, represented in both modern and Maori artworks.

Examples of the traditional Maori art form by tohunga whakairo (Maori master woodcarver) John Mutu, and sculptor Tim Wraight, can be found at Motueka's Te Awhina Marae. Nelson is also home to Brian Flintoff, master carver and maker of traditional taonga puoro (Maori musical instruments).

Wood turning is represented by a number of skilled and committed artisans making traditional and contemporary pieces.

Bob and Anne Phillips, located at Mapua Estuary, are leading woodturners producing works from sustainable New Zealand woods.

Nelson is home to New Zealand's first private woodworking school, the Centre for Fine Woodworking, which offers tuition in a range of woodworking methods and furniture design.

Kindly sponsored by Nelson Pine Industries

John Shaw working in his studio. Photo: Centre for Fine Woodworking

Knock on Wood

"Furniture making is a constant riddle, balancing engineering, aesthetics and function," says woodworker John Shaw.

Competing with sophisticated manufacturing processes means quality is also critical. "We have really got to be offering something more," he says.

"Individual design is about finding out what the owners want, what their expectations are, what sort of room the table and chairs will go into, what space a hall table will become part of, or what art piece a particular shelf or cabinet will set off."

A long-established art form, furniture making is enjoying a modern renaissance.

"At the moment we are experiencing a reaction against mass produced furniture and there is much interest from both students wanting to learn fine furniture making, as well as those people wanting to purchase and own a hand crafted piece of New Zealand furniture," says John, who founded the Centre for Fine Woodworking with fellow woodworker David Haig.

The art of wood is very strong in Nelson, with John attributing the relaxed pace of life as suiting those who work in the medium.

"Woodworking is a very meditative process. You need to take your time to achieve quality."

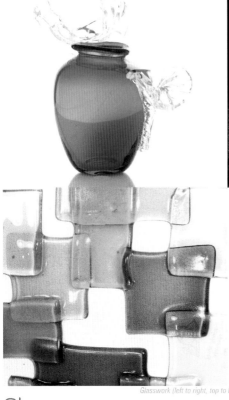

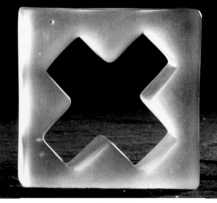

Glasswork (left to right, top to bottom) Flamedaisy, Lynette Cain, Frances Woodhead and Höglund Art Glass

Glass

Nelson is well known for contemporary glass art. Swedish couple Ola Höglund and Marie Simberg-Höglund established the Nelson region's first glassblowing studio in 1984.

Their European craft caught peoples imaginations and very soon they had taken on the role of educators as well as artists.

One glassblower to benefit from their support has been Anthony Genet of Flamedaisy Glass Design, who once said: "When you buy a piece of Höglund Art Glass, you're not just paying for the glass and the time it took to make it, you're paying for the 30 something years of international experience that comes with it."

Glass is unique as a media in that it is one of a very few substances that has no crystalline structure. Although it appears solid, it is in fact a substance that has passed from a hot, molten liquid to a cold rigid state without structural change.

As well as watching molten glass being shaped, visitors to Flamedaisy in Trafalgar Square can learn to blow their own Christmas bauble.

Other artists working with glass include Lynette Cain who is renowned for her glass jandals and Kiwiana items and Frances Woodhead who established the Nelson Glasshouse using 100% recycled fused glass. Given the amount of sunshine in Nelson, glass works well here. "It's the way it interacts with light," says Frances. "It's got energy in it."

Kindly sponsored by the Nelson Regional Economic Development Agency

Ola Höglund at work. Photo: Höglund Art Glass

Glass Act

While many artists consider their work an extension of themselves, a glassblower's art is literally made from their life force.

"As an artist I am fascinated by making a form with the human breath," says glass artist Ola Höglund, who established Höglund Art Glass in Nelson with wife Marie in 1984.

Twenty five years on, the business the couple started in the township of Richmond is an internationally renowned brand, with celebrity clientele including Sir Elton John, Bill Clinton, Olivia Newton-John and Mohammad Ali.

Ola knew at an early age that working with glass was his destiny.

"The first time I saw glassblowers at work, I was just a young boy. I decided straight away that when I grew up I was going to be a glassblower myself."

Ola describes being a glassblower as like being a musician.

"Every day is spent practising and training. Glass is so technically difficult to work with and has a life of its own.

"Every time I blow a piece of glass I am trying to improve from the previous time, and every time I get just as frustrated and feel the need to do it one more time."

Weaving & Textiles (left to right, clockwise) Fibre Spectrum, Mary Andrews, Sue Bateup (detail) and Marlin Elkington

Textiles & Weaving

The use of textiles around Nelson is as eclectic as the range of people who make the region their home.

From flax weaving to slinky catwalk styles and streetwear, the local scene offers something for fans of both the traditional and the cutting edge.

The creative textile bonanza traces its roots back to 1974, when the Nelson Polytechnic School of Weaving opened. Students learned the traditional crafts of spinning, dyeing, pattern drafting and weaving under the watchful eye of Anna Corea-Hunt.

The weaving school was later integrated into the Nelson Marlborough Institute of Technology School of Arts.

As the institute's training changed from weaving to a more general approach to textiles, artists using textiles in mixed media work and fashion emerged.

Weavers like Sue Bateup continue to work at the loom, creating exciting palettes with dye pots and making a commercial success of the artform. Other artists have taken those traditional skills and integrated weaving into other artworks and mediums.

Across the region traditional Maori flax weaving has seen a resurgence as weavers work to pass on the skills of their craft.

Fibre Artist Mary Andrews. Photo: Nelson Mail

Spinning a Yarn

Where there's a wool, there's a way for fibre artist Mary Andrews.

Mary spins, weaves and felts garments, accessories and interior décor items from scratch, sourcing fleece from local farmers.

"I work from a desire to transform raw fibre into functional art," she says.

"I like to start from as raw a material as possible so that I'm doing everything along the way. When I have finished, I am the only one who has altered the fleece from the time it's come off the sheep."

Mary, who runs popular felt making workshops from her home, was a founding member of the co-operative fibre craft gallery Fibre Spectrum, established by a group of weaving school graduates in 1987.

She credits working co-operatively as the key to maintaining a commercial presence for fibre arts over the years.

"There's been a huge revival – it was just about extinct 20 years ago."

Sharing retail duties at the Fibre Spectrum gallery enables members to keep in touch with the public and what they're looking for.

"We'll also have people come in and say 'I just wanted my colour fix' and that's as important to us as the sales – it makes us feel the craft is valued."

Photos: Daniel Allen (top) and (left to righ) Craig Potton and Ursula Spring Thomas

Photography

Surrounded by serene landscapes and transforming light, it's no wonder Nelson is home to a strong community of photographers.

The arrival of former Londoner Daniel Allen in 2003 has been particular poignant for the region's creative community.

Promptly establishing himself as one of the South Island's top advertising photographers, Daniel has also turned his lens to documenting artists' work, contributing to a growth in quality archiving of works.

As well as working for some of New Zealand's premiere lifestyle magazines, Daniel works locally on projects for Craig Potton Publishing, WildTomato lifestyle magazine, and shoots his own conceptual work.

Daniel's images have been included throughout this guide, alongside stunning photograph's from Ursula Spring Thomas in the Golden Bay section and selected shots by Craig Potton.

Kindly sponsored by the Nelson Regional Economic Development Agency

Craig Potton. Photo: Nelson Mail. Photos (below): Craig Potton

Frame of Reference

Artists represent our environment, presenting us with possibilities and reminding us of realities.

Ironically one of the critiques of landscape photographer and publisher Craig Potton's work is that it is too perfect. "People will say 'it's too blue'," he says, using the example of an image of the moon rising over Tasman Bay, below.

"But you actually look out there and it's amazing. The blue is exactly that blue, but our habitual eyes have filtered it down. We dumb down our perception. "

"Art does that — you see the world again afresh."

Sometimes it takes experiencing nature out of its context inside a gallery to see it for what it really is.

One of New Zealand's foremost landscape photographers, Craig is also well known as a passionate conservationist and activist. But when he has his camera in his hand it's for art, not politics.

"The photograph has to work as a composition," he says. "But nature is a subject that undoubtedly I have a lot of feeling about. If photography can heighten peoples' positive appreciation then that's great, but they should like it first and foremost because it's a good photograph."

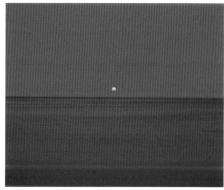

A performance at Saxtons Feild (above) and The Wellington Uklele Orchestra (below). Photos: Nelson Mail

Film & Performance

While the final credits have well and truly rolled on the Lord of the Rings trilogy, its legacy lives on in Nelson's creative community and surrounding landscape.

A number of Nelson artists worked on props and sets; photographer Craig Potton did the trilogy's stills photography; local craft brewer Craig Harrington brewed Sobering Thought, the special one percent beer for Hobbiton and the Prancing Pony Inn; the late Jens Hansen and son Thorkild designed The One Ring; and Nelson itself provided two of the trilogy's most spectacular locations — Mount Owen as Dimril Dale hillside, and Mount Olympus as the Eregion Hills and rough country south of Rivendell.

Blessed with a mild climate, outdoor concerts and performances are often set amongst Nelson's stunning landscapes.

Neudorf Vineyard and Woollaston Estates hold regular vineyard concerts, Shakespeare productions often tour the region's parks in the summer season, and the Nelson City Council runs an annual Opera in the Park.

That rings a bell...

It takes a lot of drive to succeed in the film industry – a concept Orinoco's Dan Hennah knows only too well.

The former fisherman and architectural draftsman had his first break in movies as a driver for Tatum O'Neal during filming of Prisoner in 1981.

Now an Oscar-winning art director, Dan and wife Chris spend a majority of their time working on film projects in Wellington, including five years on the Lord of the Rings trilogy. Their children Nancy and Daniel also worked on the films.

Some of Dan's other film credits include The Frighteners, Sinking of the Rainbow Warrior, White Water Summer, Savage Islands, The Rescue, Mesmerised and King Kong – proving his philosophy, "if you keep doing it 100% someone notices."

Mount Owen (above). Photo: Craig Potton. Dan & Chris Hennah with the Oscar (below). Photo: Nelson Mail

Suzie Moncrieff. Photo: World of WearableArt™

The World of WearableArt™

At the bar of art ingenuity, Suzie Moncrieff's creative spirit sits on the top shelf.

In 1987 the sculptor-turned artistic director had a vision of taking art off the wall to adorn the moving body. And with a prize donation of $1,000 from local café owner and visionary Eelco Boswijk, what is now known as the Montana World of WearableArt™ (WOW®) Awards Show was born.

Set in the country community of Spring Grove, WearableArt™'s inaugural show in 1987 premiered before an audience of 200. Twenty-odd years on, it entertains an annual audience of more than 35,000 and attracts entries from designers and artists throughout the world.

Now one of New Zealand's premiere events, Suzie's community fundraiser has journeyed from a leaky tent to an international stage, offering designers over $100,000 in prizes

and media profile. The show is judged by New Zealand's top creative talent, often joined by international names such British media personality Janet Street Porter and fashion designer Zandra Rhodes.

While the main event is now held in Wellington, WOW® is still planned and judged in its Nelson headquarters within the World of WearableArt™ and Classic Cars Museum, which was opened in 2001, showcasing a dazzling array of former entries. Exhibitions are changed quarterly and are accompanied by audiovisual material to give a glimpse of previous shows.

WearableArt™ is now a creative genre in its own right and has given artists in Nelson, New Zealand and throughout the world an opportunity to showcase their creativity on an international stage.

Suzie says she loves the creative freedom the show provides people to give life to their wildest imaginings.

"We need more quirky things in life — it gives the world more colour."

Nelson WOW®'s Supreme

While the WOW® Awards have gone global, local designers are still regular finalists and two incredibly contrasting characters have taken out the major award in recent years.

In 2004, then 18-year-old Claire Prebble won the supreme WOW® Award in a poetic end to the show's Nelson reign.

The shy and humble Golden Bay teen with an unimaginable talent for weaving metal, had been entering the awards for a decade, having become a finalist in the Children's Section with a work titled 'The Junk Fish' when she was just eight.

Her 2004 entry, 'Eos' (Evolution of the Spirit) was the culmination of two years of dreaming and 1,000 hours of creating.

The following year, vivacious Nelson Green Party politician and creator of 'festoonery' Mike Ward had just been voted out of office when he got voted in as the supreme winner of the 2005 WOW® Awards.

'The Emperor's Entourage' consists of two large wearable canvasses and is a play on the Hans Christian Anderson tale, The Emperor's New Clothes. The front depicts what the wearer sees in the mirror when they dress up in their glad rags, but from behind we see them as they are 'in all their plump gorgeousness'.

Mike can often be found selling his 'festoonery' at the Nelson Saturday Market.

Eos by Claire Prebble (above) and Mike Ward with The Emperor's Entourage (below). Photos: Nelson Mail

Literary Arts

They say a picture speaks a thousand words, but using a few words to create a picture is an art form in itself.

The literary arts may not be as prolific as the visual arts in Nelson, but there are some exceptionally talented writers around. Nelson poet Cliff Fell has received prestigious national accolades for his collection 'The Adulterer's Bible', which saw him receive a Creative New Zealand grant to write his second book.

Others recognised in recent Montana New Zealand Book Awards include poet Jessica Le Bas, who won the Best First Book — Poetry award for 'Incognito', and historians John and Hilary Mitchell, who took out the history category for 'Te Ara Hou — the New Society'. Children's author Melanie Drewery is best-known for her Nanny Mihi series, which are designed to give children easy access to Maori language and culture. The books are illustrated by Nelson artist Tracy Duncan.

In publishing circles, Nelson's Craig Potton Publishing punches above its weight and is renowned for quality and creativity. Nikau Press specialises in books relating to the top of the South Island, such as 'The Suter; One Hundred years in Nelson', by Susan Butterworth.

Kindly sponsored by The Nelson Mail

Nelson Books. Photo: Daniel Allen

Maurice Gee. Photo: Dominion Post

More than Words

Like paint, words crafted well capture the essence of place and personalities.

Maurice Gee's move to Nelson in 1975 proved pivotal for his career. It's here, where he lived for 14 years and raised his two daughters, that the famous novelist believes he began to pen his best work.

Maurice is one of New Zealand's most distinguished authors and was recognised as one of New Zealand's 10 'greatest living artists' within the Arts Foundation of New Zealand Icon Artists in 2003. His other accolades include: Prime Minister Award for Literary Achievement, numerous Montana New Zealand Book Awards, James Tait Black Memorial Prize, NZ Children's Book of the Year, and two honorary doctorates of literature.

Now 77, Maurice returned to Nelson in 2006 to live a bit more quietly and privately. He still writes, now focusing on fantasy fiction for children.

The Nelson region features prominently in many of Maurice's works, including 'Loving Ways', 'Ellie and the Shadow Man', 'Blindsight', 'Prowlers' and 'The Burning Boy' – the latter being set in "Nelson in disguise" so he could make a few things up.

"Nelson's a place that I've lived in, a place that I know, a place that I enjoy and I'm fond of. If I'm writing about Auckland or Wellington and I want to suddenly make my characters goes provincial I immediately think of Nelson, so I send them."

Robin Slow. Photo: Nelson Mail

Maori Arts

Whatungarongaro te tangata,toitu te whenua hoki. (People disappear, but the land remains).

Traditionally there was no separate word for art in the Maori language, because it was such an integral part of everything. "Art is not separate from us, it is part of us," explains Golden Bay artist Robin Slow.

"The materials, tikanga (processes) and the end products are symbolic of relationships between us as people and the place where we stand on the land."

Maori art documents the histories, struggles and triumphs of our tangata whenua (people of the land).

While Maori art has raised the profile of culture in local communities, and throughout the world, whether it has raised understanding is open to debate.

Robin says for visitors and Pakeha (European) New Zealanders to truly appreciate Maori art, they have to look at it in its cultural context, rather than from their own.

In a short visit, this is difficult to do. But what is key to understand is that Maori art isn't just about the aesthetics, it's about the journey or process as well.

Maori histories and stories are not legends viewed as mystical tales, they represent and document knowledge, histories, thoughts and emotions.

"It's a way of thinking and relating to a situation, a place, a time, or who and what we are."

Taonga Puouro (above). Photo: Brian Flintoff. Brian Flintoff & Richard Nunns. Photo. Nelson Mail

Instrumental Journey

Two Nelson artists have been instrumental in resurrecting the ancient voices of Aotearoa (New Zealand) by researching and recreating taonga puoro (Maori instruments).

Alongside the late North Island composer Hirini Melbourne, musician Richard Nunns and carver Brian Flintoff have over the years repaired the broken thread of traditional knowledge through laborious research and discussion.

Richard describes the instruments they have unearthed as "cellphone to the devine."

He has contributed to soundtracks for the movies The Lord of the Rings trilogy and Whale Rider. He also regularly performs all over the world, working with artists from a vast range of genres — from classical and jazz, to contemporary Maori and Irish music.

His work saw him presented with an honorary doctorate of music from Victoria University in Wellington in 2008. Read more about the story in 'Taonga Puoro — Singing Treasures'.

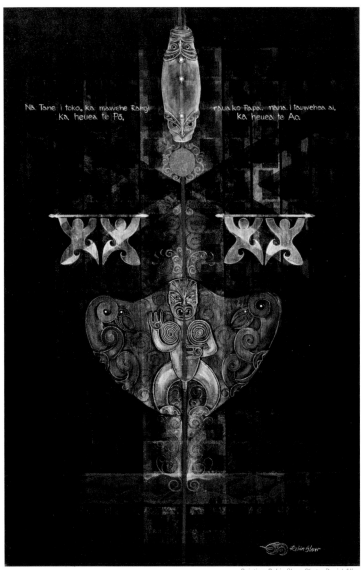

Na Tane i toko, ka mawehe Rangi
ka heuea te Pō.

rāua ko Papa... mana i tauwehea ai,
ka heuea te Ao.

Painting: Robin Slow. Photo: Daniel Allen

According to Maori legend, Ranginui (the Sky Father) and Papatuanuku (the Earth Mother) were once joined together and the earth lay in darkness. One day one of their sons, Tane Mahuta, saw a glimpse of light and set about separating his parents so he could see more.

In the following story Golden Bay artist Robin Slow describes Tane's search for light and how the eventual separation of his parents formed Kokowai, the sacred red earth that has been used in both modern and traditional painting in Nelson and throughout New Zealand.

Nothingness, Te Kore

From the Nothing came the Beginning. And the Gods sang the world into existence.

From Te Kore came Te Po, the Night, the Great Night, The Dark Night, the Long Night, the Night to be Felt, and the Night Unseen.

From Te Po came Te Ao, the Light, at first no more than a glow-worm-light, a light just seen. Sudden light, Te Ra came and warmed the heavens.

From Te Ao came Ranginui, time and space. From Te Po, with warmth and dust, Papatuanuku, the Earth Mother was created.

Ranginui, the Sky Father, encircled his arms around Paptuanuku and held her close.

Tane Mahuta lay in the damp darkness with his brothers between his parents. Tane tucked under Ranginui's arm. Ranginui made the slightest of movements and Tane saw, ever so quickly, a wonderful light.

The Light of Te Ao.

Tane wanted more of this wonderful light.

Lying on his mother, Papatuanuku, Tane drew his knees up to his chest and placed his feet on his father. Slowly he pushed, and the more he pushed the more light shone through between his parents. The more light, the stronger became Tane.

With one final push Tane separated his parents, and the world became light: the full light of Te Ao Marama.

With the light came the separation shadows. The parents were separated forever from each other.

In these shadows were the brothers. Tawhiri Matea loved his parents greatly and was angry with Tane's actions. He fought with his weapons of the winds. Tangaroa of the Oceans pushed himself into white foam against the land surface. Haumaietiketike protected what he could by placing it safely below the surface of the land. Rongo Maraeroa tried to heal the wounds created by the fighting brothers. Ruaumoko the unborn lay in the womb of Papatuanuku - he was the protector of fire and the great earth shaker. Tu Matauenga fought all, reducing all in front of him to nothingness. He was the only one in the form of a man. It was he who sliced the sinews of his parents when they were stretched to breaking point. The final separation was created with this action.

The parents' blood dripped from them, the first blood at the beginning of time. The blood dripped from Ranginui on to Papatuanuku. The blood seeped into the dust and formed Kokowai the sacred red earth.

Tane gathered the Kokowai from the most sacred parts of Papatuanuku, sculpted and created the first woman, breathing life into her.

Kokowai was gathered and ground, used as a covering, a protector, painted on bodies, buildings and stone walls, and used to create the sublime kowhaiwhai patterns.

Tapu Te Parapara Maunga overlooks Mohua (Golden Bay), and from this mountain flows the river Te Pariwhakaoho, red with the blood from the separation of Ranginui and Papatuanuku. In the sands at the edges can be seen the glow of red washed there with the cleansing waters.

On flows the river, past the old pa site, to the sea. Washed ashore, the Kokowai stone of various tones can be found. A treasured resource.

When Pakeha arrived the stone was dug out, collected and ground for paint. Throughout Aotearoa, railways and rooftops, barns and fences were painted with this material, always to protect.

Today we remember that whatever we create and whatever the form, from the beginning there was the thought, music, movement, moulding, sculpting, and materials, woven together in a whariki that lies across Te Ao Marama, this world of light we live in.

- Robin Slow

Aotearoa: New Zealand, Kokowai: Red oxide coloured earth material, Kowhaiwhai: Scroll painted patterns usually painted on rafters, Koauau: Maori flute usually made from wood or bone, Maunga: Mountain, Papatuanuku: The Earth Mother, Pakeha: European, Ranginui: The Sky Father, Tane Mahuta: A son of Ranginui and Papatuanuku, Tapu: Sacred, Te Kore: The Nothingness, Void, Te Ao Marama: The world of light, the human world, Te Ra: The Sun & Whariki: Mat.

Integration of Art

The architecture industry is an imperative partner in Nelson's creative community, integrating art or designing spaces to showcase it.

When architecture and art come together, they inspire, says Ian Jack, of Irving Smith Jack Architects.

"Whether in the grand gesture or the smallest detail, their mutual reinforcement brings enrichment and delight."

The architectural process is about collaboration, says Arthouse Architecture's Min Hall. "Architecture, besides being an art form in its own right, presents prime opportunities for incorporating and showcasing the work of other creative people."

The Nelson i-SITE Visitor Centre complex at Millers Acre Centre Taha o Te Awa, which won a New Zealand Creative Places Award, is the perfect example of the meeting of artistic and architectural minds. The project was a collaboration between Ian Jack, Nelson City Council, and Nelson artists John Shaw, Mike Hindmarsh, Gavin Hitchings, Grant Palliser, Tim Wraight, and Jim Mackay.

"The building and the art combine to instruct the visitor on our place, our people and how we came," Ian says.

The Schaeffer Loft in Mahana by Arthouse Architecture was designed with showcasing the owner's extensive collection of contemporary New Zealand art in mind. The project also involved collaborations with a number of local artists in the fabric of the building; including Glenn van der Leij's stainless steel and timber kitchen, and Tim Wraight's carved and inlaid linen cupboard doors.

The Schaeffer Loft (above). Photo. Arthouse Architecture. Grant Scott Door Handle (bottom left). The Nelson i-SITE at Millers Acre Centre (bottom right)

"The artists' work help turn what are often mundane activities into memorable events," Min says.

Ian agrees art can enrich an environment by introducing something unexpected, drawing on the use of a Grant Scott door handle in one project.

"The things we touch are so important. This one small piece of threshold art celebrates arrival, builds anticipation, and puts you in expectation of something special."

An occasion at Fairfield House. Photo: Nelson Mail

Nelson Cathedral. Photo: Nelson City Council

Heritage

The marriage of art and heritage has been a long and happy union in Nelson.

Over the years many Nelsonians have advocated for the protection and restoration of heritage buildings, and it is thanks to them that the city retains so many of its historic buildings.

Art has been incorporated into a number of public buildings throughout the years and the Nelson City Council aims to include it in all new capital works as well. The Aratuna Normanby Bridge is a good example of this (page 52C).

One of the earliest examples of public buildings incorporating artwork is Nelson's most photographed cultural landmark, Christ Church Cathedral. The Cathedral, standing guard staunchly above the city on Church Hill, features beautiful stained glass. It is also the showcase venue for the biennial Adam Chamber Music Festival, and hosts a special arts service during the Nelson Arts Festival.

One of the many famous heritage buildings in Nelson with a Historic Places Trust Category One rating is Fairfield House. Fairfield is the backdrop to some of

Nelson's happiest times, including the popular annual Jazz in the Park picnic in the early New Year and a number of other festivities and art workshops.

In nearby Brougham Street you'll find another heritage house, Melrose House. Surrounded by historic woodland, it hosts a variety of functions and events.

Broadgreen House in Nayland Road, Stoke is a good example of a colonial residence and offers a glimpse into a vanished way of life. It is surrounded by the impressive Samuels Rose Garden that boasts over 3,000 roses.

A number of cultural trails have been formed throughout the city's historic and creative precincts. For more information on Nelson region's cultural heritage call into The Nelson Provincial Museum on the corner of Trafalgar and Hardy Streets.

A number of art and heritage trails around the city can be found on www.ncc.govt.nz including the Eel Walk and the Trevor Horne Trail. Information panels can be found at many sites in the city. The i-SITE Visitor Centre, the Nelson City Council and Nelson Provincial Museum are all good sources of information and many key arts and heritage sites can be found in this guide.

Kindly sponsored by Nelson City Council

Collections

Around 95% of The Suter Art Gallery's extensive collection has been acquired through gift, bequest or donation of funds from locals, making it a truly community collection.

The Suter was built as a memorial to the second Bishop of Nelson, Andrew Burn Suter (1830-1895), who was left incapacitated for the last five years of his life by a stroke.

During this period he discussed his "long cherished wish" to present an art gallery to the people of Nelson, so immediately after the Bishop's death in 1895, Amelia Suter began to realise her husband's dream, gifting land, money and her late husband's art collection to establish an art gallery.

Building on Bishop Suter's donation, the collection has grown to over 800 works of art in a variety of media. It has a strong regional focus, with highlights including New Zealand's largest collection of watercolours by 19th century landscape artist John Gully (1819 – 1888), a collection of works by Sir Tosswill Woollaston (1919-1998), one of the founders of modern art in New Zealand to whom this Nelson Art Guide is dedicated.

A significant collection of works by ceramic artists of national and local renown is also held. - *Anna-Marie White*

Woollaston 101 collection exhibition 2008 (below), Refine: WOW® Inspires Nelson Art exhibition opening 2007 (bottom right) and image collection store room (bottom left). Photos: The Suter Art Gallery

Don Neilson. Photo: Daniel Allen

Art of Collecting

When you buy art from the hand that created it, you are handed a key. Together you unlock the work's story and write the next chapter. The story is endless, because art lasts forever, the key just changes hands.

On entering Don and Pat Neilson's home on Nelson's Port Hills, guests either look forward or to the left. Art lovers look left.

Ignoring the stunning Tasman Bay vista spread in front of them, their attention is instead captured by a two-storey wall stacked with rows of paintings.

Over almost three decades, Don has gathered an expansive collection. A former commercial artist, Don moved to Nelson from Invercargill in 1980. His art collecting career began not long after, when he stopped by one of the Nelson Independent Art Group's annual exhibitions in the Queens Gardens. 'Purple Haze', a painting of Tahunanui Beach by Colin Higgins,

caught his eye. The rest is history ... and on Don's walls.

A tour around his home reveals an amassed collection that includes the works of Nelsonians like Anne Rush, Sally Burton, Brian Strong and Katie Gold, complimented by a raft of primarily South Island artists and a few international pieces.

Each has a story about when and why he bought it: "That never took off, I really thought it would," he muses, walking past one. While purchases are generally made on the basis of "something I like the look of", there is an element of challenge to Don's hobby.

"I do like to try and pick art that will increase in value — something that you buy for a couple of hundred and it ends up being worth a few thousand."

Don credits Nelson's creative energy as inspiring his hobby. If he hadn't have moved here, he wouldn't have collected, he says.

"I would've probably had a few bits, but nothing like this."

Artist in action. Photo: Daniel Allen

Coffee (above). Photo: Daniel Allen. Painting by Shona McLean (below)

Nelson, New Zealand   S McLean

Café Culture

Freshly ground coffee is the unsung hero of the Nelson arts industry. Many an early morning recording subtle transitions in light, and late nights putting the final touches on exhibition works have been fuelled by the world's most popular legal drug.

The relationship between Nelson's artists and coffee was firmly ground in 1961, when Eelco Boswijk opened Chez Eelco Coffee House in Upper Trafalgar Street (now the House of Ales bar).

Reputed to be New Zealand's first real café, 'The Chez' introduced much more than a kerbside haven for caffeine addicts to Nelson. It nurtured the minds, inspiration and careers of those who would become among some of the area's most famous creative personalities. One of Nelson's most successful painters, Jane Evans, had her first solo exhibition at the café in 1966.

The legacy remains. Dozens of Nelson cafés and retailers have since offered local artists free exhibiting space.

A democratic approach is applied, with exhibitors ranging from amateur to established artists. Morrison Street café has embraced this philosophy, with regularly changing exhibitions it's, a launching pad for local artists.

Pomeroys Coffee & Tea Company has been roasting beans for over 15 years and their window has long been a billboard supporting artists exhibitions and events.

These days, Sublime Coffee & Roastery on Haven Road is often inhabited by artists meeting for an early morning brew or mid afternoon chat to run over exhibition ideas and has a great spot to relax on the veranda.

Cuisine

While modern society is now embedded in the digital age, so much in Nelson remains crafted - not just art; but also cuisine, wine and beer.

Fresh, seasonal and sun-drenched describes the unique taste of Nelson. It is the produce created by the blend of people, landscape, climate and sea that gives Nelson its well-deserved reputation.

From fresh summer berryfruit to shellfish straight from the sea, bright flavoured tomatoes, crisp autumn apples and award-winning olive oils, Nelson cuisine follows the availability of seasonal produce. It starts in early spring with the excitement of fresh, succulent scallops dredged from the sparkling waters of Tasman and Golden Bays. Later, the spring weather brings succulent strawberries and delicate spears of asparagus from the Waimea Plains and by Christmas, the first of the boysenberries match the summer supply of fresh, local snapper for a Pacific-style celebration.

In Nelson you can eat breakfast over the water, visit a berry farm, catch your own salmon and dine at a vineyard all in the same day. At markets you can buy luxurious handmade chocolates, gourmet preserves, German sausages and wild game.

In restaurants, chefs excel at using local produce to create memorable dishes, best teamed with the region's award-winning wines in front of a view to remember.

From fine dining to casual cafés, Nelson offers lively and creative eating experiences featuring the very best in seasonal celebrations.

A number of the region's restaurants and bed & breakfasts serve local, organic produce. To source your own visit the Nelson Saturday Market in Montgomery Square, Founders Farmers Market on Friday evenings, the Motueka Market on Sundays, or the Saturday Golden Bay Market. Or stop by one of the many roadside stalls and berry farms - and remember to use the donation box! - *Jude Gillies*

Tasman Bay Scallops accompanied by Nelson wine (top), Local berries (bottom left) & Greenshell Mussels (bottom right). Photos: Nelson Tasman Tourism

Angela Bone. Photo: Nelson Mail

Food for thought

Whether you're an artist or a chef, the number one ingredient for the creative recipe is passion, says chef and lodge manager Angela Bone.

To create the best you need the best, and for this reason good quality ingredients and materials are a quick second to passion.

"Nelson produce is some of the best, it's so amazing what we have on our doorstep," says Angela, who can source all the fresh produce she needs on the short drive from Motueka township to Motueka River Lodge.

"It's so much fun, I can get everything from fresh asparagus and organic free range eggs to stonefruit."

Like the artists that surround her in the nooks and bays of the Tasman region, Angela draws her creative inspiration from colour. "Colour is really important to me - being a chef is a type of artist."

In her cooking classes at Motueka River Lodge, Angela teaches confidence in the kitchen. "It's about getting together a group of like-minded people and sharing experiences. They learn that the kitchen isn't a scary place. I'm very much into being able to make mistakes and then being able to fix them."

Like her creative contemporaries, Angela has her favourite artistic tools. "A very sharp knife and an even sharper sense of humour."

Wineart

In both wine and art, a bit of good taste doesn't go astray.

Winemakers are artisans in their own right, handcrafting rich and subtle flavours into what is often referred to as Nelson's 'liquid sunshine'.

As with the region's artists, our wineries work collectively, while still retaining their individuality. Nelson Wineart represents 25 of the region's wineries, and promotes the art of winemaking Nelson-style.

"All the Nelson wineries are boutique producers – and family-owned," says Wineart's Gisela Purcell.

"The Nelson cellar door experience is as a result a very personal and individual experience."

There are two distinct wine growing areas in the Nelson region – the Moutere Hills and the Waimea Plains, each with quite different soils and weather conditions.

The gravel-threaded clay soils of the Moutere Hills that attracted the region's founding ceramic artists are favoured to build pinot noir and chardonnay. Like any

good man, the pinot is lovely and rich, while the chardonnays have a flavour that will render even the staunchest of ABC (Anything But Chardonnay) drinkers charmed.

The Waimea Plains' stony soils and high sunshine hours make it particularly good for aromatic wine varieties, for which Nelson is particularly noted. UK wine magazine Decanter hailed them as New Zealand's best.

Nelson's wines have supported local artists beyond the occasional lubrication of the creative process.

Many wineries feature local art in their cafés, galleries or cellar door environs. The Wineart collective is also a strong supporter of Nelson's regional art museum, The Suter Art Gallery, providing wine for exhibition openings and other special events.

Pick up a copy of the Wineart map for a comprehensive guide to all of the region's wineries.

Kindly sponsored by Wineart

Vineyard in Redwood Valley (above). Photo: Seifried Vineyard.
Opposite page (left to right, top to bottom): Row of Grapes. Photo: Nelson Mail. Wine Vat, Glass of pinot and local hospitality. Photos: Wineart

Beer Essentials

Ever dunked a square of chocolate in your beer to see what it tasted like?

One could safely assume not, so welcome to the world of craft brewing. It's a world where experimentation with flavour is God. Where hops, yeast and barley make friends with the likes of coriander, coffee, tangelos, elderflower and vanilla pods.

"We are fairly experimental," understates Tasman Brewing's Craig Harrington.

"You have got to have a passion for it, you have got to enjoy what you do and experiment with flavours."

The art of brewing is in being bold, fun and open to ideas. There are seven craft breweries in the Nelson region, which has a longstanding brewing history. New Zealand's second commercial brewery was opened on the corner of Hardy and Tasman Streets in 1842, Nelson breweries were among the first to export beer in the mid 1840s, and the region was at the forefront of a regional brewing renaissance in the 1980s. Due to Nelson's ideal latitude and

climate, all of New Zealand's commercial hops are grown here.

A trail of brewer-operated pubs scatter the region, including Golden Bay's The Mussel Inn, and Nelson's Founders Brewery (recognized as one of the top organic breweries in Australasia) and The Sprig and Fern taverns, whose name comes from the sprig of a rugby boot and the nation's revered symbol of sporting prowess, the silver fern.

You won't find a big screen, gaming machines and pool tables at the Sprig — just a Tejas Arn artwork leading you to the tavern's door and a welcome smile behind the bar which has some 20 brews on tap.

"Craft beers are a taste your palette will develop — it's about getting out there and having a go," Craig says.

As well as at local bars, locals and visitors can have a taste at quarterly beer fetes and an annual craft beer festival at Founders Heritage Park.

The Sprig & Fern Tavern (above). Photo: Daniel Allen

Opposite page (left to right, top to bottom): Brewing at Founders Brewery. Beer taps. Photos: Founders Brewery. Motueka Hops. Photo: Nelson Tasman Tourism. Pouring a pint at a Beer Fete at Founders. Photo: Nelson Mail

Accommodation

Accommodation providers play a role in the arts industry far beyond offering a bed to weary cultural explorers.

Boutique lodgings are pivotal in fostering connections between their guests and artists, recommending creative places and people to visit. Many have extensive personal collections that they showcase for their guests' enjoyment and inspiration.

The Nelson region is home to a broad range of accommodation. Guests can select from luxury country lodges, inner city hotels, motels, character bed and breakfasts, homestays, farmstays, backpackers, hostels, and camping grounds. Here you can spend the night in an orchard, a 19th century colonial residence, an architecturally-designed eco-lodge, or a boot.

In the city, Consulate Apartments features local art in each of their stylish apartments, and Rutherford Hotel also does so in some of its executive rooms. You can stay within

architectural art with a castle stay just up the hill at Warwick House, or those looking for an enviable local art collection matched with quintessential Nelson views and hosts should stay at Wakefield Quay House on the waterfront.

Grand Mercure Nelson Monaco has a jeweler in its High Street village, and Wilsons Abel Tasman's two lodges feature heritage photographs telling the history of the national park and the family's longstanding connection with it.

Neudorf Hall is one of a number of bed and breakfasts run by local artists. The home of sculptor Michael MacMillan and partner Jackie offers guests the opportunity to live amongst his work and the couple also has plans to showcase others' artwork.

"Sculpture can look completely different in a home than in a gallery," Michael says. "If you are living in the environment a piece can grow on you."

Monaco and relaxing by the sea (above). Photos: Nelson Tasman Tourism

Opposite page (top left to right, clockwise): Balcony view from Wakefield Quay House. Photo: Elspeth Collier. Wilsons Abel Tasman. Photo: Wilsons Abel Tasman. Warwick House. Photo: Warwick House. Consulate Apartments. Photo: Grant Stirling. Neudorf Hall. Photo: Daniel Allen. Grand Mercure Nelson

Photos: Nelson Tasman Tourism

Experience Our Place

When travelling, people are interested in seeing beautiful places and beautiful things. Nelson is in the enviable position of having a plethora of both.

As well as inspiring its locals, Nelson's lifestyle and famed climate has drawn artists from around the globe who have visited, fallen in love with our place, and then adopted it as their home. At last count some 350 working artists lived here.

Nelson Tasman is home to three extraordinary national parks and countless beaches, bays, walkways and mountain biking trails. Activities such as kayaking, sailing, quad biking, golf, and kite surfing are all accessible just moments from the centre of the city. On the weekends, visitors and locals merge at a string of local markets, handpicking produce, crafts and cuisine.

Viewing art is a way for people to interpret and learn about a region's history, culture, and landscape. Buying art is a way you can take a piece of a place home with you. But what is most important when discovering a new place is meeting its people. The accessibility of Nelson's artists means our visitors don't just purchase a product, they gain an experience – a meaningful connection with a local, a creator and a storyteller.

We are lucky to have such a wealth of artists here who give colour and life to the fabric of our place. While our landscapes and climate are world renowned, Nelson's greatest asset is its people. We hope you enjoy meeting them.

For visitor information see www.NelsonNZ.com or stop by one of the region's visitor centres.

Kindly sponsored by Nelson Tasman Tourism

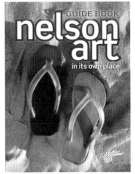

Arts Marketing

The Nelson Bays Arts Advocacy & Marketing Trust was established in 1993 by artists for artists. As well as publishing the biennial Nelson Art Guide, Arts Marketing carries out a number of projects to encourage the arts to flourish in the Nelson Tasman region. Projects have included a series of fine art exhibitions, Arts Markets and the creation of a Nelson Artists Studio in Wellington to promote the regions creativity. For more information visit www.nelsonart.info

Arts Marketing thanks all those who helped create this Art Guide providing information, guidance, inspiration and resources.

A special thanks to the following organisations for their support:

Nelson Art Studio in Wellington Airport (top). Photo: Nelson Tasman Tourism. Refine exhibition (left). Photo: Arts Marketing. Sixth edition of the Art Guide Book, featuring Lynette Cain's glass jandals (middle centre). Bayleys Twilight Arts Markets (right). Photo: Maria Bennich.

Farewell Spit. Photo: Craig Potton

Index by Category

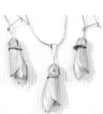

Index by Name